PARKINSON'S & RECREATION

ONE MAN'S JOURNEY THROUGH PARKINSON'S...SO FAR

DENNIS JERNIGAN

SHEPHERD'S HEART MUSIC, INC.

Published by Dennis Jernigan/Shepherd's Heart Music, Inc.

7804 West Fern Mountain Road

Muskogee, OK 74401

Jernigan, Dennis: Parkinson's & Recreation — One Man's Journey Through Parkinson's...So Far

ISBN (paperback): 978-1-948772-21-1

ISBN (epub): 978-1-948772-20-4

Cover Design: Jones House Creative

Edited by: Darren Thornberry

Interior Design: EAH Creative

All songs (words and music) written by Dennis Jernigan unless otherwise noted.

To my wife; to my children and their spouses; to my grandchildren; to all who experience life with Parkinson's or any type of affliction; to all who need a little dose of hope and joy; to my God Who gives me grace to endure...

PROLOGUE

I am a man of faith who follows Jesus Christ. Even if we do not share that faith, my hope is that you, the reader, would come away from having read this book with an understanding of some of the lessons I have gleaned since being diagnosed with Parkinson's four years ago. I've only just begun the journey and it is rough at times, but I am determined to enjoy that journey no matter what!

> "It's important that everyone knows I'm so much more than the bad things that happen to me...You can't wait until life isn't hard anymore before you decide to be happy."
>
> — JANE MARCZEWSKI-CLAUDIO
> (NIGHTBIRDE)

When I first had the idea to write a book on my life with Parkinson's, the working title was "Parkinson's Moments." The reason for this title was simple: Parkinson's gives me many memorable moments of pain and suffering but, at the same time, affords me many more moments of sheer joy and laughter. Parkinson's disease is quite a paradox in my life. Incidentally, another title I toyed with is "No Walk in the Parkinson's." Meh.

A paradox is "a seemingly absurd or self-contradictory statement or proposition that when investigated or explained may prove to be well founded or true; a statement or proposition that, despite sound (or apparently sound) reasoning from acceptable premises, leads to a conclusion that seems senseless, logically unacceptable, or self-contradictory; a situation, person, or thing that combines contradictory features or qualities" (Google dictionary).

The more I learn to live with Parkinson's, the more of a paradox it becomes. How can pain and suffering coexist with sheer joy and laughter? They coexist, at least for me, based upon a spiritual point of view found in the Biblical text of Romans 8:28.

> "And we know that God causes all things to work together for good to those who love God, to those who are called according to [His] purpose."

After reading that verse, I had to ask myself the question, "Is PD part of the 'all things' portion of that scripture?" My conclusion? Yes. And if that is so, I believe God can use Parkinson's for my good and will give me grace to endure whatever it brings my way. The best news of all is the fact that God wastes nothing. He does not waste our sorrows. He does not waste our suffering. He does not even waste our failures. I have discovered that God is with me every step of the way through Parkinson's. That is an important component to my ability to find joy and peace in the midst of the foggy moments and physical suffering that are often symptoms of PD.

This book is not a scientific treatise on Parkinson's and what causes it or an exhaustive explanation of PD. I am actually a bit shaky (pun intended) on the cause of and treatments for the illness. I know as much as my neurologist and various Parkinson's-related websites tell me. What I am trying to say is this: I am no scientist, not a neurologist, and Parkinson's affects people in different ways. This is MY journey.

Parkinson's is not a good thing, but God uses it for my good. Parkinson's is no laughing matter, but I find myself constantly laughing at the way Parkinson's brings joy to my life and to the fabric of our family tapestry. Parkinson's is an ugly thread God has, for some reason, allowed to be woven into that tapestry and somehow made it a most beautiful facet of this journey we call life.

After coming to that conclusion, I knew I could not call the book "Parkinson's Moments" because it is so much more than that. Since I am choosing to see it as a good thing — to make lemonade out of the lemon of PD — I find my attitude, mood and overall sense of well-being rejuvenated...recreated!

Immediately, I thought of one of my favorite comedy shows, the very popular and often absurd CBS series, "Parks and Recreation"! After a series of laughter-inducing Parkinson's moments, I knew I had to call the book "Parkinson's and Recreation."

Recreation is commonly defined as "activity done for enjoyment when one is not working; refreshment of strength and spirits," but my personal definition literally means to recreate one's point of view, which brings refreshment to one's entire being. Rather than seeing Parkinson's as an insurmountable mountain of a death sentence, I choose to see it as a mere molehill that happens to be part of my journey and is intended to bring me an even greater depth of life.

I am often reduced to laughter due to the symptoms of the illness as well as to the way people respond to me when they find out I have Parkinson's. I have come to find the great benefit of using Parkinson's as an excuse...for pretty much anything I say or do...objectionable or otherwise! Having lived several years with the disease now, I have found humor and laughter and joy to be vital and beneficial to my well-being.

That all sounds so deep and philosophical, but the simple fact of the matter that caused me to call this book "Parkinson's and Recreation" is a no-brainer. It's just pretty dang funny!

Dennis Jernigan

ONE
PARKINSON'S AND RECREATION

"You don't stop laughing because you grow older. You grow older because you stop laughing."

— MAURICE CHEVALIER

"When you can laugh at yourself, you are free."

— TED LODER

have Parkinson's Disease. I received that diagnosis on January 28, 2019, and I will share more about that period of my life in the following chapter. As I have shared that information with different people, all express deep concern and many respond as if they just found out I had received a death sentence. The truth is I have not received a death sentence. I have a choice as to how I can respond to the diagnosis. I can either wallow in self-pity or I can use it for good. I choose to use it for good and find that humor goes a long way in helping me live my life to the fullest with joy.

PD is a degenerative disease. Degenerative means "a disease or symptom characterized by progressive, often irreversible deterioration, and loss of function in the organs or tissues" (Google dictionary). In the simplest of terms, my body — brain and all — is deteriorating due to my brain's inability to produce dopamine... the "feel-good" chemical neurotransmitter. In one sense, I feel I am literally losing my mind...and I might as well enjoy it! After all, I have been told on numerous occasions that, due to my faith in Christ and my belief that He can change any human heart, I have lost my mind. Now I have something to blame for it!

My purpose in writing this book is to refresh my mind and body and to see my life as not something to be dreaded but to be endured well and lived out as a grand adventure despite my circumstances. My hope is that, as you read the book, you will discover what I have discovered: Parkinson's (life's circumstances) can actually come in quite handy! For instance, when caught cheating at a game with my family, I have learned to play "The Parkinson's Card." More on that later...

Let's talk a bit about what Parkinson's is...and what it isn't. Parkinson's disease is a long-term degenerative disorder of the central nervous system that mainly affects the motor system. It's a progressive disease marked by tremor, muscular rigidity, and slow, imprecise movement, chiefly affecting middle-aged and elderly people. It is associated with degeneration of the basal ganglia of the brain and a deficiency of the neurotransmitter dopamine. It is NOT a death sentence! The symptoms usually emerge slowly, and as the disease worsens, non-motor symptoms become more common.

Cognitive and behavioral problems such as depression, anxiety and apathy may also occur in many people with PD. Parkinson's disease dementia becomes common in the advanced stages of the disease. Those with Parkinson's can also have problems with sleep and sensory systems. The motor symptoms of the disease result from the death of cells in a region of the midbrain, leading to a dopamine deficit. The cause of this cell death is poorly understood. Collectively, the main motor symptoms are also known as parkinsonism or parkinsonian syndrome. (Thank you, Wikipedia!)

I have some of the following symptoms:

• Tremor: can occur at rest, in the hands, limbs, or can be postural. I have tremors in my right hand only. At times, it feels as if the fingers of my right hand have a mind of their own due to their involuntary movement. It often appears that I am rolling an imaginary set of coins with my right hand. When I play the piano, the three right-most fingers will not work, but I have discovered that if I wear a pressure wrap for tennis elbow injuries, I can use those fingers for about 40 minutes before I wear out and they, once again, become useless.

One interesting and often very funny fact about my hand/arm tremors is that when people ask me to show them my tremors (yes, people actually do this, lol!), my hand usually doesn't shake at all. It's as if it has a weirdly satisfying mind of its own!

My hand tremors intensify when I am watching a suspenseful show or movie or a close basketball game, when I am feeling overwhelmed in a group of people (more on that later) or when I am cold, but they become uncontrollable and obvious when I join hands with another person...especially during prayers at mealtimes! After one such prayer, my son, Ezra, looked at me after the "Amen" and said, "Dad, it's like you have a party going on with your hand. That's your party hand!" My right hand is affectionately known as my party hand by my family...and I LOVE it!

In a similar vein, I was recently at a birthday party for my grandson, Mark, when my son-in-law, Shaun, turned to me during a festive moment and said, "Mr. J! We need your jazz hands!" I laughed so hard I almost fell out of my chair...and then laughed even harder when I lifted my hand and it refused to tremor! I tell you...it has a mind of its own!

• Muscular symptoms: stiff muscles, difficulty standing, difficulty walking, difficulty with bodily movements, involuntary movements, muscle rigidity, problems with coordination, rhythmic muscle contractions, slow bodily movement, or slow shuffling gait. I have experienced occasional symptoms of this nature but have an easy time with walking…and even running for short spurts with my grandchildren.

Recently, our family gathered for Sunday lunch at my mom's home. Several of my grandchildren were playing tag and asked me to join in. My wife, Melinda, said, "Oh, honey! Don't do that! You might fall!" I, of course, ignored her and quickly discovered I can no longer outrun my grandchildren. I was immediately tagged and became "it." Feeling the need for speed (I love Top Gun and Top Gun: Maverick!), I ran after the nearest grandchild with my something-other-than-cheetah-like speed…and face planted into the ground. The left side of my face felt the first impact, followed shortly by my left shoulder, left elbow, left hip, and left knee. My grandson, in shock, asked, "Are you ok, Grandpa?"

I moaned and said, "Yes…I am fine…just don't tell Grandma…"

The very next day, the effects of that face plant culminated at the local swim and fitness center where I swim on weekdays. As I stripped and picked up my swim shorts, I lifted my right leg to put on said shorts and felt a deep tinge of fiery pain as the muscles in my lower back suddenly decided they could no longer hold my body up. It felt as if my lower back had sprained, and had decided to go on strike! It took me two weeks to get over that one. I have since decided to heed my dad's sage advice dispensed to me a few years prior to his death: "Remember, you're not 18 anymore."

• Sleep: early awakening, nightmares, restless sleep, or sleep disturbances. I have a difficult time sleeping since the Parkinson's diagnosis. For most of my adult life, I had gotten by on five or six hours of sleep per night and was very active and full of energy. Parkinson's put an end to that. I do not experience nightmares, but I deal with other sleep symptoms. Judge me if you must, but I have come to see Valium and Ambien as necessary and helpful friends! I sleep seven to eight hours each night now and wake up feeling refreshed.

• Whole body: fatigue, dizziness, poor balance, or restlessness. I keep a daily schedule to help me maintain good mind/mental health but am usually mentally done by noon each day, especially if writing has consumed much of my morning time. I don't experience much dizziness and have few balance issues, but I often am restless. I feel restless if I am not doing something creatively or recreationally, like writing music or books, mowing the lawn, fishing or working on the fantasy forest my wife and I have created for our grandchildren. If restlessness is a symptom of PD, I have had the disease for most of my life!

• Cognitive: amnesia, confusion in the evening hours, dementia, or difficulty thinking and understanding. I experience moments of confusion and difficulty thinking when I feel overwhelmed with technical issues. I have discovered that I can conveniently be excused from doing a task I was asked to do by playing "The Parkinson's Card."

"I forgot" tends to get me out of sticky situations. Just saying…

• Speech: difficulty speaking, soft speech, or voice box spasms. I have moments of fatigue when I know what I want to say but my tongue and my brain do not seem to be on the same page. It can be frustrating when I know exactly what I want to say but my tongue will not say it…and I become super-frustrated when people try to finish my words for me! • I have trouble from time to time with weakness in my voice, coming across as soft-spoken. I find it easy to sing high or low notes but difficult to sing in my mid-range — especially when I try to sing softly. Most of the time, I feel it is easy to speak, but my voice and speaking capacity are not what they were even four years ago. I sound like I have PD whenever I listen to my newer podcasts as opposed to my speaking voice from past live worship recordings.

• Nasal: distorted sense of smell or loss of smell. I have always had a weak sense of smell…or a high tolerance for bad odors!

• Dribbling or leaking urine. I attribute moments of this to just getting old.

• Mood: anxiety or apathy. I experience moments of anxiety but quickly deal with them by reminding myself that God loves me and that He is with me and that my family loves me and is with me, too.

- Facial: jaw stiffness or reduced facial expression. I noticed this when I renewed my driver's license shortly after my diagnosis. I look like a zombie.

- Other common symptoms: blank stare, constipation, depression, difficulty swallowing, drooling, falling, fear of falling, loss in contrast sensitivity, neck tightness, small handwriting, trembling, unintentional writhing, or weight loss. I catch myself staring blankly into space and find such moments especially annoying when I am talking with someone face to face. It gives the appearance that I am not "present" in the moment. I feel present but do not appear to be.

I'll be honest. One of the biggest sources of frustration with PD is constipation. I know. TMI...but it affects me emotionally more than I realized it would. MiraLAX and an abundance of fruits and vegetables bring, shall I say, great relief!

I deal with depression by speaking the truth to my own mind. I rarely feel depressed. I have no difficulty swallowing. If I drool, I see it as a positive. If the drool comes out both sides of my mouth, I know I am walking in perfect balance. (Old drummer joke: It is also a way to determine if a stage is level.) I do not fear falling any more than the next person. I have no loss of contrast sensitivity and no small handwriting, but I do have moments when I feel my neck tightening. I writhe only intentionally, lol, when wrestling with grandkids and I experience no weight loss. My weakness for soft serve vanilla frozen yogurt sees to that.

Basically, my symptoms are normal and were put into proper perspective for me soon after I received my initial diagnosis. When a medical professional asked me to describe my Parkinson's symptoms, I shared honestly with him. His response? "Jernigan, you just described getting old. You don't have Parkinson's. You're just getting old!" This did more for my emotional and mental health than almost anything anyone has done for me since the diagnosis.

My hope for this book? That you would find joy in whatever

circumstance of life you find yourself. I use Parkinson's. It does not define me. I just choose joy…and I love to laugh…even at myself. And another little secret of mine? I take great delight in my children finding the light of humor in the darkness Parkinson's tries to bring. It makes me feel loved!

TWO
MAINTAINING INTIMACY WITH MY WIFE

"Spirituality is not a formula; it is not a test. It is a relationship. Spirituality is not about competency; it is about intimacy. Spirituality is not about perfection; it is about connection. The way of the spiritual life begins where we are now in the mess of our lives."

— MIKE YACONELLI

One of the most difficult things about PD is that it affects intimacy with my wife in every way: emotionally, spiritually, mentally and physically. True intimacy is she and I saying to each other, "Here is my heart. Into-me-see."

In November of 2018, I was not doing well physically and mentally. I hadn't been diagnosed yet, so we didn't know what we were dealing with. What was becoming painfully apparent to me was that my wife needed a break.

Melinda is such an amazing woman. She is a caregiver extraordinaire. She knows the basic needs of all our children, their spouses, and our grandchildren at any given moment. She keeps me posted on how the family is doing and makes sure everyone stays connected. On top of that, she is my biggest cheerleader and the most ferocious advocate for me, protective and proactive and perpetually concerned about my health and well-being. This just seems to be a huge part of who she is. Even in my foggy state of mind, I could see the tremendous weight upon her shoulders and the tremendous toll it was taking on her soul.

As Thanksgiving 2018 drew near, I felt I needed to step into the fray caused by the uncertainty surrounding my illness in a practical way that would bring much needed refreshment to her soul. I told her she needed to get away from it all. So, I firmly suggested that she go spend a week with her mom, Sheila, the best mother-in-law in the world, and that she take one of our daughters with her. Melinda balked at first, telling me she would not be able to enjoy herself due to her deep concern for me. Sensing this would be her main argument, I rallied our children and came up with a plan.

Within two hours of our home, we had five of our children, their spouses, and nine grandchildren. My point? The kids would take up the slack for Melinda so she could enjoy herself and get refreshed while away. We took away her excuses for worrying about me! The children would check in on me several times a day, provide meals when necessary, and the grandchildren would provide refreshment and joy for my soul with periodic visits.

What was such a blessing to both Melinda and to me was how quickly the children jumped on board with the idea. They ALL encouraged her to go spend time with her mom and to give herself permission to enjoy herself for a while, be pampered, get some care for her own soul, and receive the gift and trust of our children making sure I would be well taken care of in her absence.

What follows is a note I gave to Melinda as I dropped her at the airport. My desire was to express intimacy with her while reassuring her that I wanted her to be blessed and to get some rest and refreshment for her soul.

Saturday, November 16, 2018
Dearest Melinda,

I know you are worried about me...but let me assure you, I will be fine while you are away. My desire is for you to forget all fear and worry and doubt about me. I have absolutely NO doubt God is in control. It will make me EXTREMELY happy to know you are being blessed with refreshment, joy, affection from your mom and Galen, and getting a good break from feeling like you need to make sure I am OK. Rest assured I have every reason to be hopeful. Regardless of whatever we find out medically, this changes nothing with Father. I KNOW this to be true.

I know this to be true, too: that I love you too much to ever purposely give you even one inkling of a reason to worry about me. My body may be ailing, but my soul is good. I know who I am, and I know Whose I am. God has me. You have me. You both have my heart.

If I need anything, I will not hesitate to ask for help...but I am honestly looking forward to writing at least a few words every day (I won't overdo it!). For some reason, the writing fog has begun to lift from my mind, and I cannot help but think Father is saying, "Write, son. Write." And what is so cool is that in the adventures of the Bairns of Bren, we are in the story together...just like the story of our life together. For the following week, imagine all God has done to get us to where we are right now. That's what I am doing this week...and let's make this a week of Thanksgiving and gratitude.

I am beyond grateful for your place in my life. We are truly one flesh, yet you are still a great mystery to me that I am not even near to finding the answers to! You make me want to see what's around the next corner of our journey...and I am so glad I am on this journey with YOU!

Please, please, please enjoy yourself this week! And I will look forward to hearing of all the memories you made while with your mom and Galen.

I absolutely love you...you have me by the heart...

DJ

She and our daughter and her mother had a very wonderful time together. They made many memories together and they still fondly speak of them and laugh at some of the funny and quirky things they experienced that week. In many ways, the healing Melinda received during that time away reverberates through her soul to this day. That brings joy and, dare I say, a bit of healing to my soul as well. Intimacy is more than a physical coupling. It is an exchange of life between two people. Life begets life and I have been so blessed by the life my wife gives me.

Intimacy is everything. Relationships are everything. Her life gives me life and I hope my life does the same for her.

THREE
THE DREADED DIAGNOSIS

"We were promised sufferings. They were part of the program. We were even told, 'Blessed are they that mourn,' and I accept it. I've got nothing that I hadn't bargained for. Of course, it is different when the thing happens to oneself, not to others, and in reality, not imagination."

— C.S. LEWIS, A GRIEF OBSERVED

I love the above quote from C.S. Lewis and I hate it. To live life is to live it fully, whether through times of bountiful plenty or times of devastating lack; whether through times of joyful bliss or times of painful, unbearable suffering. Life is to be felt to the fullest. To feel life to the fullest means to live every moment as if it were one's last.

I want to savor the pleasant aroma of the fresh bread my wife is baking. I want to remember the stench of the dirty diapers produced by my children and grandchildren, which made me feel I needed to be wearing a hazmat suit and gas mask. Both scents are a necessary part of life. How could I ever enjoy the sweetness of the rain had I never endured the bitter dryness of the desert?

It has been my joy to share the testimony of how God delivered me from something the world does not see as sin and to hear from thousands of people who were sincerely helped by that testimony, but it has been my honor to bless and express love to those who have cursed me and spewed hatred at me as a result of that very same testimony.

My memories of the many wreckages of my life that were somehow incredibly salvaged have taught me to value every aspect of life. Like the time our twin boys came nine weeks early and we nearly lost them…and how on that very same night the physician advised me to call Melinda's parents to get to the hospital ASAP since she would probably not make it through the night. The other side of that experience taught me to value even moments of impending doom, how to mourn apparent loss with my entire being and how to be grateful when life somehow finds a way.

I have had broken bones; a ruptured Achilles tendon; a leg pierced by a 12-inch spike, effectively pinning me beneath the wheel of a farm tractor; dreadfully painful rotator cuff surgery on both shoulders; and both knees replaced (the tip of a long, extended iceberg, lol). I have endured heart-wrenching scorn and literal persecution due to my faith and have endured some of the deepest moments of despair a human mind can face from hidden childhood sexual trauma culminating in being groomed for a homosexual encounter by a trusted counselor. I would say I know a bit of what it means to suffer, but I still contend my life has been blessed beyond what I deserve.

"Never to suffer would never to have been blessed."

— EDGAR ALLEN POE

One of my favorite quotes on life is from Helen Keller:

"Life is either a daring adventure or nothing."

I love that quote. It almost captures my heart for what life means to me. Almost. I have adapted a personal version of this quote that has influenced the way I think of a life lived fully and felt deeply:

"Life is either a grand, daring adventure or it is nothing at all."

— DENNIS JERNIGAN

There are endless experiences, both good and bad, that have made my life an absolutely grand adventure. As a result of simply choosing to live my life to its fullest, I thought I had experienced true suffering…until I was diagnosed with Parkinson's. What follows[1] is the journey of coming to the Dreaded Diagnosis.

In early August of 2018 — almost one year after my dad's death — I was feeling somewhat back to normal regarding my overall mental and emotional well-being, but I began to experience excruciating pain in my right knee. About four years before, I had gone through surgery to replace my left knee. It did not take the orthopedic surgeon long to review my x-rays and explain my pain was due to all the cartilage being worn away in my knee and that I would need to have the knee replaced. I must add at this point that during my first knee replacement, the pain meds caused me to experience panic attacks. With Melinda at my side in the hospital in the days following that first surgery, I would tell her when my mind was inundated with fear. All I said to her was, "Speak truth to me."

She immediately began telling me all the good things that were true in my life. She went down the list, beginning with the fact that she was right there with me…that I had nine amazing children… that I had 11 awesome grandchildren…that God was right there with me…that I could declare the Word of God to my own soul. After only a few moments of her speaking truth to my mind, the panic attack would just be gone! For the year following my first knee replacement, we would have many such moments of me waking up in sheer panic and Melinda faithfully speaking truth to me and bringing calm to my soul.

For that reason, I dreaded the second knee surgery, but the physical pain became the driving force behind my decision to go through with it. Of course, the surgery was successful, and, after only a few weeks of therapy, I was walking again pain-free. But something just didn't seem right.

Although my physical pain had been alleviated, my mind seemed to be in a fog. At first, I simply attributed it to the effects of the pain meds following my surgery. In several public ministry times, I found myself physically and emotionally exhausted after wonderful moments of corporate worship. Rather than the usual euphoria I had always felt after such moments, I felt dread.

By November of 2018, it had become a strain to sing. At times, my voice just was not there. Raspy and hoarse replaced what was formally clear and pleasing. Again, I assumed it was due to the intubation required during my knee surgery and that my voice would return with time. It never returned. After experiencing an ENT threading a tube with a camera on the end through my nose, I was able to see that one of my vocal folds had a deep indentation in it...like the indentation a surgical intubation might cause. The ENT told me it might take up to 18 months for this type of trauma to heal. Losing my voice was one of the most heart-wrenching middle-of-nowhere moments I have ever experienced. My mistake was in believing that my voice was part of my identity. Reality was that God was about to take me on an incredible journey that makes all the persecution I have ever experienced feel like a walk in the park.

During the final months of 2018, I continued to battle an ever-deepening mental fog. At times, I could form words in my mind but could not get my mouth to speak those words. It became difficult to walk without feeling like I was in slow motion. To be honest, I thought that this must be how a zombie feels! My self-awareness of these issues and natural introverted personality made me not want to be around people at all.

It was also during those fall months of 2018 that we began to notice a slight tremor in my right hand, specifically the three right-most fingers. Once again, I went to see my orthopedic surgeon assuming the tremors were caused by nerve damage I possibly suffered during a rotator cuff surgery three years before. After a nerve test on my arm that felt like electroshock torture, my surgeon told me there was damage but nonsufficient to cause the tremors. He suggested I schedule an appointment with a neurologist. When I asked why, he simply and matter-of-factly said, "It is my opinion that you are experiencing the onset of Parkinson's Disease."

My heart sank and my mind went into full-on denial mode. My brain deteriorated into hours of foggy wilderness. My tremors increased. My speech became plodding and slurred and I sank into major depression. I began to lose weight. People noticed my delayed response times in conversation. Christmas of 2018 became one of the most painful periods of my life.

While at an annual family reunion in December, I felt so self-conscious around people that I spent most of that reunion walking around outside with my youngest grandchildren. While I LOVE being with my grandchildren, I dreaded the now-normal questions from family and friends in whom I had no doubt about their love for me.

"Are you ok, Dennis?"

"What's wrong with you, DJ?"

Although we had received the initial diagnosis of Parkinson's, we needed to have that officially confirmed by a neurologist. Needless to say, trying to get an appointment with a specialist was a major undertaking. In November of 2018, we were referred to a neurologist but were not able to get an appointment until 2019! I continued to suffer and go downhill. By the time of my appointment, I had lost more than 40 pounds and my brain had sunken into a continual fog, making conversation and ministry next to impossible for me. I had absolutely no stamina.

Finally, January 28, 2019, came. After looking at my charts and MRI results, the doctor simply said, "You have Parkinson's."

I felt like I had just been handed a death sentence, yet I felt a weird kind of relief from the constant state of mental denial I had been trying to sustain over the past few months. Bottom line: "They" do not really understand what causes Parkinson's. For some reason, the brain stops producing dopamine. Dopamine is a neurotransmitter, which is associated with reward-motivated behavior. In simple terms, it is a "feel-good" neurotransmitter (chemical messenger) that floods one's brain when something good is experienced.

The doctor went on to explain that I could live another 30 years and people might not even notice I had the disease. He immediately prescribed daily doses of dopamine and told me if my depression and tremors lessened, then I had Parkinson's. I took my first dose that afternoon. My mood lifted and my tremors lessened. Middle-of-nowhere moment. I had Parkinson's disease.

Melinda and I decided we would honor the remaining concert and ministry events for the coming year but would take no new engagements in order to allow my mind to heal. We also felt we needed to be honest with our family and friends and with those to whom we ministered. Truth sets us free. The first step of truth is honesty. While I believe that was the right thing to do — I still believe that — I was not prepared for what was to follow.

Both Melinda and I began to be inundated with "cures" for Parkinson's. The sheer number of remedies suggested by well-meaning people was overwhelming. If I had tried to implement everything suggested, I would not have had enough time in the day to get to each one!

One of the most difficult things for me to endure even a year and a half down the road from the initial diagnosis is the way people respond to me when I tell them I have Parkinson's. I understand people love me and that they want what is best for me, but sometimes it feels like I have just told them the world has ended and that I am on death's bed. Here is a brief set of examples of what people have said to me that did not bring me much comfort.

"Oh, Dennis! I'm so sorry!"

"Oh, man! How terrible!"

And my favorite, "We're so sorry for what you are about to go through. We recently lost a parent to Parkinson's and what you are facing is absolutely horrible."

Long story short: Rather than allowing Parkinson's to define me, Melinda and I decided to see it from the King's point of view. It is our view that this is not a sickness unto death but a sickness unto God's glory. Our goal? Using Parkinson's for the kingdom of God. He wastes nothing. I find my relevance and purpose in my relationship with Him and not in the failing of my physical body! I plan to find God in the middle-of-nowhere of Parkinson's!

Even before the confirmation of the diagnosis, Melinda and I began to make plans to face this head-on. We are determined to live this life in an abundant way, giving God thanks during the storm...giving God thanks for the opportunity to experience an ever-deepening outpouring of grace and intimacy with Him.

Practically, we have recognized the need for discipline in my life as a means of continuing to renew my mind. The truth is still the truth regardless of my physical or mental state! One of the best things to do when dealing with Parkinson's is to exercise. For the first four years following my diagnosis, I swam 14 laps a day, Monday through Friday each week. Due to eczema from chemicals in the pool, I have switched to stationary bike, weightlifting, and Rock Steady Boxing to start each day.

My weekly schedule is set in stone, yet open to spontaneous altering as needed. On Mondays I write scripts for podcasts and post short videos on social media. On Tuesdays I record podcasts and post them for listeners. On Wednesdays I write and post a week's worth of daily devotions for my Patreon team members. On Wednesday evenings I lead worship and teach and minister in our home. We incorporated our home as All In All Church and minister to a small group in our home each week.

On Thursdays I get a massage and physical therapy to maintain my ability to move properly. My main issues right now are the muscles and tendons in my neck and shoulders. My therapist is a strong man who puts me through intense sessions of loosening those components in my neck and shoulders, even using a Gua Sha tool to scrape deeper and deeper into those most difficult places to loosen and bring relief. The scraper reminds me of a miniature version of a Klingon battle-axe! I have discovered I have a very high tolerance for pain, but one day he had to press so extremely hard and deeply into my neck that I came close to begging him to stop. He asked if I was ok. My response...it's a guy thing to say...was, "Now I know what the opposite of an erection is."

He laughed hysterically and said, "I completely understand." TMI?

Also on Thursday afternoons, if I feel energized enough, I write whatever the Lord brings to mind, whether music or fiction or whatever. Fridays I simply devote myself to being creative in some way.

As of this writing, my depression has lifted. My stamina has increased. I feel direction and purpose. I daily think of ways to minister to my family and am very conscious of leaving as huge a spiritual legacy for my children and grandchildren and generations to come as possible.

Sleeplessness is a side-effect of Parkinson's so falling asleep can be quite the battle even with sleep meds. Being around people still makes me battle feelings of being overwhelmed, but I force myself to be with people despite my feelings. I know I need people even though it would be easier to avoid them.

Just as I did with the stinkin' thinkin' from my younger days, I am doing with Parkinson's. I am renewing my mind daily by putting off the lies of the enemy and replacing them with the truth of God's Word. I am reorienting myself and my awareness of God's truth even in the midst of this battle. One of my personal rules is that I do not get to call myself something my heavenly Father does not call me. I am His son, and I am loved, no matter what.

Being told I have Parkinson's was like being trapped in a wave on a beach, that wave tossing me and turning me so violently that I can't tell up from down. To reorient myself, I simply need to stand up on Solid Ground. Jesus is here as my Solid Rock even in the middle-of-nowhere of Parkinson's. He is still with me. He has not moved. He has not changed. His love for me absolutely refutes and casts down fear.

We were not promised an easy life or that we would not have to suffer, but we were promised we would be given grace to endure and that we would never be left alone. Why Parkinson's? Why me? Why not Parkinson's? Why not me? Many have suffered far worse life-altering things than I have, but I have a great cloud of witnesses I can look to for encouragement when the enemy's lies would have me give up rather than fight the good fight of faith.

Noah built an ark and saved humanity even while others mocked him for doing so.

Moses led the children of Israel out of bondage and to the promised land even though he himself never got to set foot there.

David defeated Goliath even when his own people doubted his ability. David committed murder and adultery, yet he is known to this day as being a man after God's own heart.

Stephen was stoned to death for his faith.

Paul was imprisoned and executed for the sake of the Gospel.

And Jesus...

Need I say more?

"Therefore, since we have so great a cloud of witnesses surrounding us, let us also lay aside every encumbrance and the sin which so easily entangles us, and let us run with endurance the race that is set before us, fixing our eyes on Jesus, the author and perfecter of faith, who for the joy set before Him endured the cross, despising the shame, and has sat down at the right hand of the throne of God."

HEBREWS 12:1-2 NASB

---

1. Taken from my book "The Middle of Nowhere"

FOUR
LAUGHTER AND A DIFFERENT POINT OF VIEW

"Perspective is everything when you are experiencing the challenges of life."

— JONI EARECKSON TADA

One of the things that has brought comfort to my soul since my diagnosis is the number of notable people who have suffered with Parkinson's disease. Don't get me wrong. I wish there was no such thing as PD. Just to know I am not alone in this journey and that others have lived meaningful, rich and joyful lives with great depth and fullness has brought me much hope for my own journey. I'll list a few. Some you already know of. Some will surprise you. Still others may shock you or give you an aha moment.

Michael J. Fox, actor, one of the funniest people on the planet and one of the most visible and outspoken champions of those who deal with PD was only 29 when he was diagnosed. He says he spent the next seven years in denial. I was diagnosed at 59 and spent about a year in denial (maybe I still harbor a bit of denial, lol).

He was on top of the world with a hit TV show, Family Ties,

and a little movie called Back to the Future when he first noticed a twitch in his pinky finger that triggered a visit to a neurologist who confirmed his diagnosis. He says, "The hardest part of the diagnosis was grappling with the certainty of the diagnosis and the uncertainty of the situation. The diagnosis was certain. The progression was indefinite and uncertain." He goes on to say, "Parkinson's is the gift that keeps on taking."

My daughter, Hannah, who lives in Australia, sent me a link to a video of Michael giving a speech in November Of 2022. The Motion Picture Academy held a special awards ceremony called The Governors Awards, presenting the Jean Hersholt Humanitarian Award to Michael J. Fox for his work in raising money to fund a cure for PD via The Michael J. Fox Foundation (www. michaeljfox.org), which has raised more than 1.5 billion dollars thus far. Michael funds research and offers encouragement to people around the world, and I am humbled by his attitude and greatly inspired by his tenacity.

He accepted the award and expressed his gratitude in a speech while tremoring and experiencing spasms and moments of vocal difficulty, saying, "My optimism is fueled by my gratitude and, with gratitude, optimism is sustainable." He exuded bravery, humility, and hope while coating it all with an endearing and disarming sense of humor. Hannah made me aware of this speech in one of our family chats. After she watched the video, she sent me this note:

"I'm weeping. Love you so much dad. I love that you and Marty McFly are the special ones. We watched the Back to the Future [movies] with the girls a few weeks ago, and I told them Marty had a party hand, too...all of the sudden, Marty was cooler than cool. They [our granddaughters] have the best G Pa on the PLANET."

Honestly, I could end this chapter there and be quite content. Knowing my grandchildren love me and my party hand is more than enough for me. If you would like to watch Michael's speech, go to https://youtu.be/dKQXDve6WiE or Google "Michael J. Fox Receives the Jean Hersholt Humanitarian Award — 13th Governors Awards."

Other people of note with PD:

- Alan Alda, who for me will always be Hawkeye from M*A*S*H. I loved the show so much that I even attended the final episode screening party at a friend's house dressed as Corporal Klinger. (Fitting? I'll let you decide!)
- Muhammad Ali, world champion boxer who lived his life after the initial diagnosis in a very public and joyful way that truly inspires me.
- Former President George H.W. Bush lived his final years with Parkinson's and a joyful demeanor.
- James Doohan — Scotty, Chief Engineer of Starship Enterprise. Read my life story, "Sing Over Me," to find out how Star Trek changed my life.

There are so many more historical, notable and positive public figures who dealt with Parkinson's, but I had to include one more for the sheer fact that Parkinson's can affect anyone. Adolph Hitler had post-encephalitic Parkinson's. When I first heard this, I found myself asking, "Does this mean I will one day have a tendency toward maniacal world domination and genocide and self-aggrandizement?"

Nope. Parkinson's did not create Hitler's worldview, nor did it create the evil in his heart. Those had already been established. I just found it worth noting that Parkinson's can affect anyone from God-fearing, people-loving songwriters like me to the leader of the Third Reich.

I do not wish to make light of another person's suffering. It is not my intention to belittle anyone who suffers with Parkinson's or any other illness, but I believe in the power of laughter and the foundation of joy from which I have chosen to live my life. Of course, I realize no two people experience Parkinson's in the same way. For some, it is debilitating. For others, it is almost unnoticeable. For some, the disease progresses quickly. For others, it develops slowly over many years. For some, the degenerative nature of the disease is a constant reminder that their body and mind are under attack. For others, it becomes a point of standing one's ground and fighting for every ounce of clarity of thought. For some, it hits late in life. For others, early in life. For me, it hit right when I was ready to really enjoy my life!

And I do enjoy my life immensely even though I have Parkinson's. Even in using the term "I have Parkinson's," there is purpose. I have IT. Parkinson's does not have ME! In other words, I have chosen to see it as something God can use for good in my life. I was diagnosed just before my 60th birthday. In the many years leading up to that momentous age, my thoughts were completely focused on seeing my dreams come true, of being able to step away from public ministry, of being able to travel to visit my family who are scattered around the world, of spending time with my wife, of playing with my grandchildren. In one sense, the diagnosis dashed all those dreams. In another sense, the diagnosis deeply enhanced all those dreams and gave me laser focused, more creative methods of seeing those dreams realized in even more meaningful ways. I may not have control over how the symptoms of Parkinson's manifest or increase as they invade the dreams of my life, but I always have a choice as to how I view them. Perspective is everything.

"The only thing you sometimes have control over is perspective. You don't have control over your situation. But you have a choice about how you view it."

— CHRIS PINE

Although I take steps to slow the progression of the disease, the reality is I experience the symptoms daily. Though I go through periods of trying to ignore them or have moments when I feel little or no symptoms, they always creep back into my life. An hour without a tremor in my right hand is seen as a victory. A day when I do not experience dreaded constipation is a victory. A few hours without a foggy feeling in my brain is a few hours of victory. Times spent with my family — especially with my grandchildren — are times of victory over Parkinson's. Early on, as a family, we decided to take on what I have already noted as the Romans 8:28 point of view. Let me remind you one more time:

> "And we know that God causes all things to work together for good to those who love God, to those who are called according to [His] purpose."

I had to take a few weeks to grieve the initial diagnosis, but there came a point when we as a family stopped walking around on eggshells regarding PD and faced it with honesty. And to be honest, humor played a huge role in breaking through the barrier of my own fears and anxieties as well as those of my family. My fear was that people would treat me with pity and as "less than." That way of thinking — I call it stinkin' thinkin' — flies in the face of my personal rule concerning what I think of myself. My rule? "Dennis Jernigan does not have the right to call himself anything other than what his Father God calls him." That means I also do not get to think of myself as less than ANYTHING or anybody! (Wait. Did I already mention this? Oh, well…I DO have Parkinson's…).

As I learned to apply that rule to the reality of PD in my life, it soon became apparent that the diagnosis, in the grand scheme of the journey of my life, is a mere blip on the screen. More of an annoyance and an inconvenience and certainly not a part of my identity in Christ as a new creation! Still, I had not realized how self-focused I had become because of the diagnosis. My mind had become so consumed with asking what if, why me, and why now that I effectively began cutting off the very thing that brings me the most life. Relationship, intimacy, knowing and being known. On one hand, withdrawing from others was out of fear of what others would think, and on the other, I did not even realize I had been withdrawing from people.

Walking in relationships with others requires both giving and receiving. It is a two-way street. We were not created to walk alone. We were wired for relationship. Without relationships, there is no life.

The Sea of Galilee in Israel is full of life. It receives rain and run-off from the surrounding hills. That same water, full of life, flows all the way to the Dead Sea via the Jordan River. The Dead Sea receives the same water, yet it's DEAD! How can that be? Even though it receives water from the Sea of Galilee, it has no outflow. There is no give and take. There is no life because it only takes in and gives nothing back! As new creations in Christ, we are intended to thrive and flourish as we walk relationally with God and with others...whether we have PD or not!

Without relationships, life is drudgery and lonely. Without relationships, nothing is shared. Burdens are carried alone. Emotional wounds are left unattended. Incredible moments of celebration are empty and meaningless without someone to share them. Without relationships, there is no joy in life. I thrive on joy! My soul is buoyed by joy in the sea of despair PD can often become. By choosing to walk in joy, the sounds of the crashing waves of the sea of despair are replaced with the laughter I share with others as we find joy even in hard times.

"A joyful heart is good medicine, but a broken spirit dries up the bones."

PROVERBS 17:22 NASB

What I have come to believe and practice throughout the course of my life that has helped me traverse the journey of Parkinson's is knowing the difference between happiness and joy.

Happiness is "feeling or showing pleasure or contentment" and is based on my circumstances. When my circumstances are good, I feel pleasure and contentment. When my circumstances are bad, I feel discouraged and like I am floundering in an ocean with no land in sight.

My definition of joy is derived from what I believe about God's love for me and presence with me. I believe God is with me through every circumstance, even moments of failure. I believe He loves me massively and likes me and likes being with me. No matter what. Knowing I am never alone goes a long way in helping me conquer fear and walk in self-control when I have moments of Parkinson's-induced anxiety. Knowing I am completely and utterly loved is the security blanket of my soul, my shelter in the storms of life, my foundational anchor from which I view the world and my circumstances. God's presence is always with me, and His love is the air I breathe. Love literally crushes fear for me.

A great example of what I am trying to convey is my relationship with my own children and grandchildren. I absolutely LOVE being with them. I adore my children and grandchildren. I like my children and their children. When we get together, one of my favorite things to do is listen to them share memories and tell stories about their own lives. It blesses me to no end to see the wonder in the eyes of my grandchildren as they listen to their parents reminisce about their own childhoods. I am reduced to moments of laughter that go deeper than the pain of my illness. I am reduced to blubbering tears of joy at the love between my children and their own children — a joy that my illness can come nowhere near. I love just being with my children and grandchildren. I don't even have to say a word. Just to be with them is enough for me. If I, as an earthly father, feel such a deep love for my children and such a deep joy at simply being with them, how much more does our heavenly Father love and enjoy being with us?

When we gather as a family, I don't want to miss a thing, so I have to be honest with myself about my weaknesses and about my point of view. I need to stop focusing on myself and on my own circumstances and focus my attention on the truth of God's Word to me and on the needs of others. My children and grandchildren do not need me to be Super Man. They just need me to be dad...to be G Pa...they just need me to BE with them. I have discovered that when I focus on God and others, my own emotional needs get met...and then some. I just need to get over myself!

One of the things, oddly enough, that helped me get over myself came from a conversation with a friend who I used to swim laps with at the local swim and fitness center (I shared this already, but it bears repeating). He happened to have a medical degree. During a break between laps, he asked me about my recent medical test concerning the possible diagnosis of PD. I told him the neurologist had confirmed a diagnosis of Parkinson's. My friend then asked me to list my symptoms.

I told him about my right arm and the occasional tremors... about the occasional moments of feeling fogginess in my brain... about the moments of walking into a room and wondering why I had even come to that room in the first place...about the occasional moments of constipation...about feeling easily fatigued at the simplest of tasks...about the constant insomnia. After listing a few more things I considered symptoms of Parkinson's, he stopped me and said very matter-of-factly, "You just described getting old. You don't have Parkinson's, Jernigan. You're just getting old!" This did more for my emotional and mental health than almost anything anyone has done for me since the diagnosis! It made me laugh — a lot — and gave me a better perspective on my illness. Life is not about me. It's about bringing love and joy to those I love. It's about where my faith lies, and it is about what is truly of value: Relationship.

"Faith gives you an inner strength and a sense of balance and perspective in life."

— GREGORY PECK

I have not shared much about the moments of Parkinson's-induced laughter as the title of this chapter might suggest. It is meant to be an introduction into why my family and I have so many moments of joy and laughter as a direct result of Parkinson's.

I am getting old...and I am ok with that...which reminds me that one of my sons, while still in high school, nonchalantly informed me, "When you're old, I'm putting you in a home first chance I get."

I recently reminded him of that, and he denies it (but one of his younger brothers has confirmed the veracity of this statement)!

FIVE
TAKING THE PISS OUT OF PARKINSON'S

"Wit, and particularly the dry, ironic, taking-the-piss sort of wit, was completely beyond them. (Do you know that there isn't even an equivalent in American speech for 'taking the piss'?). Yet here in Britain it is such a fundamental part of daily life that you scarcely notice it."

— BILL BRYSON

I know. I know. The title of this chapter may seem vulgar or inappropriate to you, but I am a country boy, and I grew up with the word "piss" being an acceptable and common word to use as it relates to urination. Recently, I learned a new phrase and usage of that word from my daughter who lives with her family in Australia.

"I'm just taking the piss out of you" is a British/Aussie quip that means "to mock or to be joking, without the element of offense." It is a way of saying, "Don't take yourself so seriously."

Learning to deal with the outward symptoms of Parkinson's with complete strangers is one thing but learning how to deal with it in my family — especially as it concerns my younger grandchildren — has been quite challenging. Since 10 of our 12 grandchildren live within visiting distance, they have literally grown up with the way we have come to process the illness and my response to it in a very natural way. They don't care. I'm just grandpa to them. All Parkinson's means to them is that grandpa has a "party" hand!

My two Aussie grandchildren have not had the advantage of proximity and physical closeness. My anxiety level shot through the roof the closer their first visit home in five years drew. The main symptom — tremors in my right hand — is unnoticeable for the most part as I go about my daily routine, but it becomes completely uncontrollable and obvious when I feel someone noticing it.

As I expressed to my Australian daughter my concerns about how she and her husband and two children might respond to my illness, she replied, "Dad. You are just dad. You are just G Pa. We have no reference point from which to respond to your illness. You are dad and G Pa. That's all you need to know."

When my Aussie granddaughters ran through the doorway from the airport gate area, they both ran to me and threw their arms around me and shouted, "G Pa!" I was in tears and immersed in a depth of joy I cannot even begin to explain. Of course, as family group hugs (which take a long time due to the vastness of our immediate family!) came to an end, both granddaughters took me by the hand, and we made our way to the baggage claim.

And, of course, my right hand began to tremor. I could feel my hand and arm movement increasing in intensity. This led to a tinge of anxiety and my fear that my granddaughter (the younger one) would be repulsed and cringe and cower in fear and want nothing to do with me.

My granddaughter DID notice...and my heart stopped. In the most beautiful Aussie dialect, she simply asked, "G Pa. Why is your hand shaking?"

I froze, but my wife, having noticed what was going on, very matter-of-factly told her, "That's G Pa's party hand! It means he's happy and that his hand is enjoying its very own party all because of you!"

Do you want to know what my granddaughter said? "I love your party hand, G Pa! You must be so happy to see me!" Tears. And more tears. And still more tears. It took the innocent response of a child to break the pride of my heart that would have otherwise kept me from enjoying my precious time with my Aussie girls. As the three weeks we spent together flew by, more references to the symptoms of my illness came up and were given the Romans 8:28 treatment:

> "And we know that God causes all things to work together for good to those who love God, to those who are called according to [His] purpose."

Over those three weeks, I invested deeply into the lives of all 12 of my grandchildren, taking every opportunity to explain to them how God can take even something as dreaded as Parkinson's and use it for good. They bought into that truth with their entire beings, and we had a blast. My party hand became like a barometer to my grandchildren that said to them, "G Pa is having so much fun! Just look at his party hand!" They even quarreled over who would get to hold my party hand during walks through the forest or games of hide and seek or even when holding hands for mealtime prayers!

Later, during one such moment, my daughter took me aside and said, "Dad. you're taking the piss out of Parkinson's. It's all good. My girls think you hung the moon. They feel you are beyond present with them...even when you feel foggy. You've really taken the piss out of it. I love you so much."

I immediately understood what she meant by that phrase even though I had never heard it before. It set my heart at ease and filled me with peace. Perhaps a better way to express it in an

American sort of way would be, "You've taken the power out of Parkinson's that it thought it had over you." I love that.

Dennis Jernigan has taken the piss out of Parkinson's! Now that's funny...and empowering! And now I need to go pee...

SIX

THE ECSTASY OF EUPHEMISM

"Euphemism is a human device to conceal the horrors of reality."

— PAUL JOHNSON

"Euphemism is a good way to talk about a bad thing."

— SMARTBLOGGER.COM

A euphemism is a mild or indirect word or expression substituted for one considered to be too harsh or blunt when referring to something unpleasant or embarrassing. For example, those responsible for hiring and firing far too frequently say, "We, as a company, are going to be 'downsizing' in the coming days." Downsizing, of course, means firing or laying off employees.

Another euphemistic-like part of our language is political correctness. Rather than being a true euphemism, politically correct language is intended to be a respectful and polite way of saying something that could be deemed offensive. For example, people have said offensive things about me concerning my belief in God's ability to change one's self-perception. "He is obviously misinformed and so emotionally wounded from his past experiences that he has some mental challenges" translates to "He is living a lie and he is crazy." I might as well be honest here. Due to my personal beliefs, I have been told on more than one occasion that I am crazy and that I have lost my mind. It might have been less hurtful if they had only said, "Dennis Jernigan has lost his marbles!"

Euphemisms are classified as figurative language, which is the "use of words in an unusual or imaginative manner." They are not meant to be hurtful. They are meant to lighten the emotional burden of the harsh realities of life. For instance, when someone dies, we feel the more compassionate and sensitive way to express that reality is to say, "They passed away" or "They're in a better place now."

One of the best euphemisms I have run across is:

"Perhaps we have been guilty of some terminological inexactitudes..."

— WINSTON CHURCHILL, TO THE BRITISH
HOUSE OF COMMONS IN 1906

What does terminological inexactitudes mean? It means, "Perhaps we have been guilty of some LIES!" Our culture is full of such amazing and preposterous euphemisms, and I find them both useful, funny and absurd!

A favorite euphemism from my own life experience is quite humorous to me. Many years ago, as I was being sedated and wheeled into an operating room for a surgical procedure, I was drowsy and mellow. Everything felt like pure ecstasy...as if I were floating on clouds. As the nurses and I turned a corner, a metal bedpan tumbled from a nearby table as my bed bumped into it and crashed to the floor with a loud, clanging, metallic sound that echoed through my trippy state. I asked, "Did someone just kick the bucket?"

The entire nursing and surgical staff burst into laughter and could not believe I was lucid enough to make such a joke. I asked, "Is that a sign? Should I be concerned?" Again, laughter and assurance that, "Everything is going to be just fine, Mr. Jernigan," which, itself, was a euphemism for, "We hope so…" Two euphemisms for the price of one!

I hope that this chapter diffuses the fear and anxiety PD often brings to people. Yes, it involves physical and mental suffering. No, PD is not fun in any way, shape, or form, but I refuse to allow it to rob me of my joy!

Finding humor in my illness is not denial. I know what I have. Joy comes in finding a unique perspective in even the difficult moments…especially in the difficult moments. When I can find joy amid my pain, that pain is more bearable. And sharing that joy with my family and friends gives them the opportunity to shoulder the burden with me.

Recently, a couple of people responded to a song I have recorded since the onset of PD in my life. Admittedly, my voice has been drastically weakened and less pleasant to listen to, but one person said euphemistically, "The song was classic Jernigan, but the performance left a lot to be desired," meaning, "His voice sounds terrible and unsatisfying!" Another said, "I really like the song, but it didn't sound like the Dennis Jernigan I know," meaning, once again, "Dennis Jernigan's voice sucks!"

One of my sons recently asked me if I wanted to play a card game with him and if I wanted to play with a handicap. I began to laugh and said, "I always play with a handicap! I have Parkinson's!"

He giggled and said, "No, not that. I meant, do you need a handicap, like an advantage given to golfers." Unintentional euphemism at its unintended best!

By now you may be thinking, *Dennis Jernigan is very unique.* I know what you really mean. You are actually thinking, *Dennis Jernigan is so odd...so weird!* Maybe that is me just projecting my own self-perceived euphemism onto you. Enough about all that. I need to take a break and "walk the dog" or "see a man about a horse." I am feeling the ecstasy of euphemism right now...or soon will be once I "relieve myself"...

SEVEN

THAT TIME I USED PARKINSON'S AS A MAIN CHARACTER IN A NOVEL

"No legacy is so rich as honesty."

— WILLIAM SHAKESPEARE

"...and you will know the truth, and the truth will set you free."

— JOHN 8:32 NASB

I have been writing fantasy novels for my children and grandchildren for years. There are many reasons for that. Explaining spiritual principles in abstract ways while taking the mind on a grand adventure leaves a lasting mark on the human soul. I enjoy fantasy and adventures of the mind. My imagination takes me to places in God's majesty and gives me jaw-dropping experiences in His presence that the humdrum living out of the expected and ordinary life cannot do.

"At all ages, if [fantasy and myth] is used well by the author and meets the right reader, it has the same power: to generalize while remaining concrete, to present in palpable form not concepts or even experiences but whole classes of experience, and to throw off irrelevancies. But at its best it can do more; it can give us experiences we have never had and thus, instead of 'commenting on life,' can add to it."

— C.S. LEWIS

When I was a boy, I longed to be rescued from sexual confusion and from sexual molestation. The only times I felt "rescued" were the dreams I dreamt every night from boyhood until the day I got married. Each night, the instant I fell asleep, I suddenly found myself aboard the Starship Enterprise...and my dad happened to be Captain James Tiberius Kirk! Each night I dreamed I was captured by aliens and was about to be put to death, but every single time this occurred, my dad — Captain Kirk — was there! His phaser set on "destroy," he quickly dispatched the dreaded aliens and rescued me! Often, I woke up at the moment of rescue, full of hope and joy, with the echoes of my dream state mother, Doris Day, singing, "Que sera, sera! Whatever will be, will be! The future's not ours to see! Que sera, sera! What will be, will be."

"Reason is the natural order of truth; but imagination is the organ of meaning."

— C. S. LEWIS

What my dreams did for my mind is beyond estimation. They transported me out of the wounded, world-weary pain of my real life to places of healing I did not think possible...and made them possible! God used my imagination to show me what His healing love could do. He used it to keep me from ending my own life on more than one occasion during the miserable course of my youth.

"Imagination is more important than knowledge. For while knowledge defines all we currently know and understand, imagination points to all we might yet discover and create."

— ALBERT EINSTEIN

My story of transformation concerning my identity can be found in my book, "Sing Over Me." I had given up any hope of changing my identity and found it difficult to believe God could love me, regardless of my perceived sexual identity. All that changed when my imagination was consumed with the overwhelming love of God. I found my old identity being swept away from my mind by God's love and my new identity being swept into my mind by wave upon wave of God's amazingly massive love for me.

"Logic will get you from A to B. Imagination will take you everywhere."

— ALBERT EINSTEIN

As you might imagine, my personal transformation was frowned upon (that's putting it nicely) by the world around me. According to the world's logic, such a transformation was not possible. What I experienced within my own mind honestly seemed to bypass my own human knowledge and led me to a profoundly different way of thinking...about everything!

"Sometimes questions are more important than answers."

— NANCY WILLARD

Of course, to say such things nowadays for all the world to hear is akin to asking to be stoned, ridiculed and silenced. It raised (and continues to do so) more questions than I was able to answer in a way in which the world/zeitgeist could be satisfied. I do not pretend to understand it all myself. All I know is that, as I began to change the way I thought about myself, my feelings began to follow suit. One moment I "felt" I was something other than a man. The next, I didn't. What I do know is that, as I tell my transformation story, it raises questions in the minds of others that cause them to wonder, "Is transformation possible for me in my situation concerning my identity?"

Many people have told me I am delusional, not "woke," in denial. Despite great opposition, I have continued to walk in the reality of what I can only say was first presented to me in my imagination. It only makes sense that I do the same thing with Parkinson's...and anything else the world throws my way. I imagine God can take something as terrible as PD is perceived to be and actually use it for my good.

"You should not look a gift universe in the mouth."

— G.K. CHESTERTON

To see PD from the perspective of how debilitating a thing it must be, but then make use of my own imagination and see it from the perspective of how exhilarating a thing it must be, opens an entire universe of possibilities for me and for my family. Rather than a dreary drudgery of an existence, a change in our point of view makes it a joyful, satisfying, grand, and wonderful adventure through a universe where self-pity and shame and sorrow are no longer the focus.

My imagination prompted me to write a three-book series called The Chronicles of Bren as a way of teaching fundamentals of faith and hope. As grandchildren began to come, I began work on another series called The Bairns of Bren in which my grandchildren are the heroes of the stories. When I was diagnosed with PD, I did not know how to explain PD to them so I wrote what would become book three in The Bairns of Bren series, "The Puzzle." In this book, Parkinson's is the antagonist (read "evil sorcerer") and I am the king of Bren on whom Parkinson casts a spell called a Mind Claw. My grandchildren are the protagonists and must figure out the puzzles of their own lives all while learning how to deal with their grandfather's malady and the symptoms of the spell cast by Parkinson.

Why "The Puzzle"?

My love of writing and of hearing great stories of people who have overcome impossible circumstances has led me to write regardless of whether those writings are ever considered great. The reason I wrote The Chronicles of Bren series and The Bairns of Bren series is simple: I wanted to leave a legacy for my children and grandchildren for generations to come. As a part of that legacy, I endeavored to write stories that depict the realities of life. Life is not easy. Life is full of sorrow. Life brings times of wounding of both body and soul. Life brings times of disappointment and even betrayal. My goal is to leave my family a legacy that explains how life, even with its many hurtful episodes, is meant to be lived with joy. And just how does one do that?

I plan to live a full and joyful life for another 20 or so years, but just in case something changes, I want my grandchildren to know me and to know how I chose to face my illness and live my life with joy rather than in fear. As of this writing, all 12 of my grandchildren are 9 years old or younger. I don't know how much time I have left, but I wanted to leave them with an allegorical message of hope and heroism that helps them conquer fear and pain in their own lives and to enjoy putting together the puzzles of their own lives.

The name Bren means "flame" in German and "sword; little drop of water...like a teardrop" in Old Norse, Gaelic and Welsh. I want to live my life with the passion of wildfire. I want to wield the sword of my faith in the face of Parkinson's disease. I want my tears to be seen as prayers to my God when I have run out of words to say to Him in gratitude of the honor of having lived such an amazing adventurous life and in thanksgiving for having blessed me with such incredible children and grandchildren.

I base all my fantasy writing of both series of Bren books on a couple of specific Scriptures from the Word of God. The first is found in Matthew 6:33: "But seek first His kingdom and His right-eousness, and all these things will be provided to you." When I seek first the kingdom of God, I must first seek the King. Jesus. When I seek Him and find Him, I am afforded the opportunity to see life from His point of view.

The second passage is Mark 10:14 in which Jesus says, "Allow the children to come to Me; do not forbid them, for the kingdom of God belongs to such as these." In other words, when I follow Jesus, I follow Him with childlike faith and discover that the grand reality of life is that this amazing adventure we call life is ALL about the kingdom of God! Amazing!

The Chronicles of Bren, Book One: Captured is an allegory of my life. Book Two: Sacrifice is an allegory of how I discovered my true identity in Christ. Book Three: Generations is meant as dreams and blessings I have had for my children.

The Bairns of Bren series is simply my message to my grand-children to live life to the fullest with great joy and to see them-selves the way their heavenly Father sees them: as more than conquerors. My hope is in knowing my grandchildren will have no doubt they are loved by me and that the presence of love in their lives would vanquish fear and doubt despite whatever they will face.

Wrapped up in all the books from both Bren series is my love for my wife, Melinda, who is truly the love of my life. I have thor-oughly enjoyed the journey with her and look forward to even more adventures, both here on this earth and in the grand adven-ture of eternity beyond.

I believe that if one sees life and all its circumstances from the Lord's point of view, insurmountable mountains become molehills. Impassable rivers become rites of passage. Unbearable grief becomes an opportunity to receive comfort. Fear is replaced with love. Rather than being something to somehow endure, life becomes the grandest adventure. You see, a life lived with the Lord ever-present at one's side sands away the bitterness of life, revealing a many-faceted treasure of great worth. Forgiveness and humility replace bitterness with the heroic heart of a benevolent conqueror. My desire, as a dad and granddad, is that my heirs would come to see themselves as overcomers.

I believe Almighty God created the human imagination as a means of revealing His nature to mankind and as a means of helping the human mind understand and begin to unravel the wonderful mystery of Who God is. The gift of imagination has helped me see how even things that are meant to hurt me can be seen from a different point of view. And perspective is everything.

"You will not think clearly about your life until you think mythically. Until you see with the eyes of your heart."

— JOHN ELDREDGE

That's probably more information than you needed concerning that time I used Parkinson's as a main character in a novel, but it makes perfect sense for a book called "Parkinson's and Recreation"!

EIGHT
MASKS

"Love takes off masks that we fear we cannot live without and know we cannot live within."

— JAMES BALDWIN

"The closing years of life are like the end of a masquerade party, when the masks are dropped."

— CESARE PAVESE

When I first received confirmation of Parkinson's, I went through quite a long phase of feeling embarrassed whenever I experienced tremors in a public setting. It was even difficult to battle this embarrassment at family gatherings where I had no doubt about the love and support that was extended to me by my family.

During moments when I felt my tremors were barely noticeable, I felt anxious...and the anxiety caused my tremors to become even more vigorous and apparent. The more I tried to hide the tremors, the more pronounced they became. My solution? Avoid public gatherings...of ANY kind! But that is no way to live. We thrive in relationships. They require both giving and receiving. By hiding from people, I was effectively cutting off the best conduit of healing — the healing power of relationships.

During this time, I went out of my way to mask the symptoms I was experiencing. My tremoring right hand stayed in my pocket. At family gatherings, I found quiet places to sit and did my best to be physically present but found it almost impossible to feel emotionally present. Masking my symptoms honestly wears me out...and, come to find out, people easily saw through my masks. All they had to do was look at my face.

There is a symptom of Parkinson's that I began to manifest in the few months before my official diagnosis called hypomimia, which is known as facial masking or masked face. What it meant for me was that I found it difficult to express emotions with my facial muscles. Basically, I found it almost impossible to use my facial muscles in a normal manner. It became almost impossible to look anyone in the eyes. For me, it felt like my face was frozen in a constant stare, or, as one of my grandsons puts it, "Grandpa, you're in a daze." And he was not wrong.

My rude awakening to this phenomenon was when I went to renew my driver's license. My intention was to pose for my picture with attentive eyes and a slight but serious smile. Imagine my horror when I received my new license and saw a frowning, emotionless zombie staring back at me! It was as if I were gazing into the open-eyed blank stare of a dead body...and that dead body was ME!

What I have since found out about hypomimia is that the symptoms can vary greatly from individual to individual. Some people find it difficult to raise their eyebrows. I find it difficult to smile. In fact, when posing for pictures with my family I am always conscious of making sure I am smiling and always disappointed when I look at the resulting picture and see a deadpan stare and a frown looking back at me.

This symptom really is difficult for me and affects my ability to maintain conversations with both family and friends and becomes an intense emotional battle when speaking with strangers. Facial masking wears me out physically.

In my life before Parkinson's (which I will call LBP from here on out), I was a zealous believer in the wonderful truth found in John 8:32:

"...and you will know the truth, and the truth will set you free."

What I had discovered in my LBP was that to get to the place of freedom in my life, I had to get to the truth. The only problem with that was that the first step required of me in getting to the truth was to be honest with myself, with God, and with others. My constant fear, before Jesus found me, was that people would discover the real truth about me...that they would see that I was wearing a mask to hide my real identity...that I was performing my way through life in order to be affirmed and accepted and loved by others.

I quoted that verse until I was blue in the face but never found freedom in it because I was unwilling to be honest. I chose to wear a mask that made me appear to be talented, kind, generous, and an all-around good guy. The truth was I battled hidden unwanted sexual struggles.

The problem with wearing masks is they become things we hide behind...like prison bars of the mind that keep the real dirt and hurt we are dealing with from actually ever truly being dealt with! The moment I confessed I struggled with unwanted sexual issues was the moment God gave me a new identity; was the moment I realized temptation does not define me; was the moment I realized I would one day be married to a woman; was the moment I decided to live my life relationally — both giving and receiving — with God and with others.

We never get to the truth until we take the first step truth requires: honest confession. The moment we are honest, the masks fall off and we are able to receive truth and freedom and healing and whatever else we need. When we wear masks, we hide from the ones who can help us. It's like having a life-threatening injury and going to the doctor. The first thing the doctor is going to say is, "Show me where it hurts." If we are more afraid of what the doctor or others might think of us when we reveal our wounded place than the process of healing, we literally derail any possibility of being healed.

What seems so strange about what I am sharing in regard to wearing masks to hide our inner wounds is that I am literally dealing with a real mask that is a physical symptom of PD! I am stepping toward the freedom truth brings — stripping away the emotional mask — by being honest about the anxiety and subsequent consequences of not dealing with the effects of something very real in my life: hypomimia!

We all want to be seen in the best of light. We often find it difficult to feel affirmed, accepted, or loved because of what we consider an embarrassing or pity-inducing frailty, weakness or failure in our lives. Everyone deals with this issue on some level. The most humorous part of this for me is that my mask issue is on full public display at all times...so just who do I think I am fooling? Only myself, it seems!

I am physically tired of trying to mask the fact that I have a malady that causes actual physical facial masking. So, I have decided to take the mask off and admit I am wearing an actual physical mask that I can no longer...well...mask!

I think I would do well at a masquerade party. Just sayin'...

NINE
MAINTAINING INTIMACY: A WORK OF ART

"I don't think of all the misery but of the beauty that still remains."

— ANNE FRANK

I am very intentional about maintaining intimacy of relationship with my wife. It honestly gives me something to look forward to and helps slow the progression of the disease. As an example, the following is a birthday letter I wrote to Melinda in October 2019 following my diagnosis:

A WORK OF ART

I will never forget the first time I ever saw you. With one glimpse of your beauty, my breath was taken from me, and my heart nearly stopped beating...yet I knew you were far, far out of my league. I saw you and your radiance as something more captivating and exquisite than the Mona Lisa. Saw myself as a formless lump of clay that could never be worthy of even being in the same room as such an amazing work of art. You were at once a complete mystery to me yet a mystery that intrigued me enough to consider pursuing...

When you spoke, all I could hear was the most melodic and romantic symphony that could have only been created by a master musician, such was your wisdom and knowledge and charm and grace. When I spoke — or attempted to speak — all I could hear was the banjo theme of a country bumpkin attempting to sound like he had never seen even one episode of Hee Haw...yet my ignorance always gave me away.

Still, you began to let me into your heart — into your world. Most of the time I felt absolutely overwhelmed at the sheer lack of sophistication I saw in myself but stood amazed at the sheer sophistication and confidence in which you seemed so comfortable magnified a thousand times in you. It was almost too good to be true — that someone like you could even acknowledge the existence of someone like me. A work of art caring for a lump of clay. Sounds so ridiculous when I say it out loud, but that is how I viewed us.

I had absolutely no framework of reference of how to treat such a priceless treasure as you seemed to me, much less a frame of reference as to how to properly and sufficiently navigate any type of romantic relationship with you. Yet, you saw something in me that I could never see. I saw it in you in droves. Worth. You were worth more than me risking hurting you by speaking the words "I love you" just to gain physical touch. I saw you as a fine piece of alabaster, fragile yet strong, beautiful beyond measure...to be cared for and valued above all else. I wanted you to feel treasured and valued...yet found it difficult to communicate that to you because I possessed neither in my own life. The lump of clay.

That you would even attempt a relationship with me made me love you all the more. The closer we became, the more fear gripped my heart and mind. How could I ever possibly give you what you needed when I felt so absolutely needy myself? I felt like a ping pong ball, bouncing from "Could it be possible to love someone like you the way you deserved?" to "If she sees me as I truly am, she will reject me." By the time we were seniors in college, I knew a day of reckoning was coming.

I will never forget the look on your face when I told you I never wanted to see you again...how broken your heart seemed to be. My reason? Better to break her heart once and for all than to drag her through years of torment and insecurity and failure and pain. After all, a work of art deserved to be displayed with other works of art...and I was no work of art. In that moment I felt more like a shapeless, formless, worthless lump of clay than ever. You seemed more exquisitely beautiful to me than ever. In my heart, I felt I had done the right thing.

Funny how God uses the brokenness of our lives to bring about the most exquisite works of art. The heartache of losing you sent me into a downward spiral that ended in a muddy pit of self-loathing mire...and Father met me there with love like I had always imagined possible but never thought possible for myself. By the time I hit rock bottom, this lump of formless clay had become so hard and brittle that it had finally shattered...but the Master Artist began to put me back together, piece by broken piece...until a mosaic that looked a lot like redemption began to take shape.

With a stroke of masterful genius, the Master Craftsman used a feeble prayer to lead me back to you. "If you want me to be married, Lord, speak that through my parents." The very next week, my parents told me they always thought I would be the first of their four sons to marry, to which I flippantly responded, "Who do you think I should have married?" Without one moment's worth of hesitation, they both said, "Melinda was the one for you."

That moment sent me reeling with hope yet simultaneously sent me careening through my thoughts with fear! Reeling with the hope that someone like you could love someone like me...and careening through my mind at the same moment the fear of being rejected by someone like you! So I asked the Lord to speak through your parents if this was truly his will...and He did.

Your mom answered the letter I wrote her and gave me permission to pursue you. A month later we were engaged. Almost a year later we were married. The complete fulfillment and contentment and satisfaction and pleasure of knowing you in every way filled my heart with more joy and hope than I thought I could possibly ever experience in this life. I thought I knew you...but the mystery was just beginning!

God was transforming me into a work of art and He was doing the same in you. I was learning how to be a man. You were learning how to be a woman. But more importantly, He was teaching us how to be a son and a daughter first...to know our identity. It was like starting at ground zero and working our way through a grand adventure of discovery...a thrilling journey called life, chock full of twists and turns and tragedies and triumphs, an epic saga and greatest love story ever told.

Still as opposite from one another in almost every way possible, yet still both valuable works of art in the Master Craftsman's hands, He was slowly teaching us the dance of romance...a divine and diverse set of steps and motions that we are still attempting to learn to this day.

We danced through the season of raising our nine children with many trips and falls along the way, but what was left in our wake — nine magnificent children — was worth every misstep and challenge along the journey.

We now dance into the latter years where children begin to marry and begin dances of their own. We are learning the precious dance of grandparenting that we get to pretty much make up along the way. What an adventure! Such adventures are always more joyful when shared with another...and I am so grateful I get to share these adventures with you!

You are still a mystery to me. A mystery I feel even more challenged to unravel with my final days. Though we face a season where my health has become the major challenge we face, we face it together. Without you, I would not...could not...last a day longer.

You are priceless to me...

You are a precious treasure to me...

You are the obsession of my heart...

You are the perfect fit for me in every way...spiritually, emotionally, mentally, and physically...

You are a symphony straight from God's heart to mine that declares, "See how much I love you, son?"...

You truly are a work of art...and you helped transform this former lump of clay into something I never thought I would or ever could be...whole...

You are the wind beneath my wings...

You make life feel like an intricate dance that truly captivates my heart...

You are the muse that inspires beauty and melody and music to my soul...

You absolutely complete me...

Though the seasons of our lives change, these things I have spoken will always remain...always...

I absolutely and honestly love you...

Happy Birthday...

DJ

TEN
PARKINSON'S MOMENTS

"Life is short, and time just flies by, so I love those moments when we're all sitting around the table together laughing and joking."

— AINSLEY EARHARDT

One of the ways Parkinson's reminds me of its presence in my life comes in what I like to call Parkinson's moments...and there are many. Recently, I was talking with an acquaintance about very surface things like the weather and the fact that we really need rain. Normal stuff. He made a comment about how dry his lawn was and asked me about how my lawn was doing. In my mind I was answering him, but in reality, my eyes glazed over in fear as I realized my brain was not processing the command to speak the answer in a timely fashion. Our eyes locked and my silence became quite awkward and uncomfortable, so much so that my friend just moved on and tried to fill the obvious void with a conversation-ending statement, "Well, have a good week," and he walked away. A classic Parkinson's moment.

At first, such moments left me feeling embarrassed and ashamed, but now I just assume they know I have Parkinson's and are being kind to me despite the awkwardness. It has taken me awhile to get to that place, but I am constantly experiencing new moments and new ways to deal with them.

One of the greatest joys of my life is having grandchildren. By the time this book is out, we will have 13! The grandkids love to play games with me, from Tic-tac-toe to Battleship, from board games to card games. The younger ones strongly urge me to let them win. I cannot comply (most of the time)! My noncompliance always produces the most amusement for me. One granddaughter tells me where I can and can't place my X or O when playing Tic-tac-toe and her frustration with me makes me laugh every time... which only amps up her frustration. Such moments eventually wear me down emotionally and mentally and often lead to me just placing my X or O wherever she strongly suggests. She knows how to lure me into a Parkinson's moment by wearing me down, assuring her of eventual victory. I live for such moments.

Her brother, old enough to understand and play card games with me, loves to play Nerts. If you are not familiar with this game, I highly recommend it...especially if you have a large family. Our family is so large that, when playing certain card games (like Nerts or Oh Heck), we use two tables. One is called The Winner's Table and the other is called — you guessed it — The Loser's Table. Whoever has the lowest score at The Winner's Table has to move to The Loser's Table for the next game. Whoever has the highest score at The Loser's Table gets to move to The Winner's Table for the next game.

Nerts is one of our family favorite card games because it involves keen mental awareness, lightning speed, and spur-of-the-moment strategy. A game of Nerts is basically group solitaire at supersonic speed, which quickly saps my mental strength and leads to many Parkinson's moments...and to the discovery of just how ruthless and competitive my children and grandchildren are. I LOVE it!

The object of the game is simple. Players race to get rid of the cards from their "Nerts" piles by building them from the ace up onto common foundations all players have access to in the center of the table. It is very much like a shark feeding frenzy! In case you don't know how to play Nerts, use this handy dandy link because I guarantee you and your family will have hours of fun in the process of racing to get rid of your Nerts pile: bicyclecards.com/how-to-play/nerts.

I was recently overjoyed when one of my grandsons told me his mom (my daughter) had taught him to play Nerts. He challenged me and Melinda to a game. I was quick to remind him that I was a very accomplished Nerts player and that he should not be discouraged if I beat him. He went right to work and very, very quickly got rid of his Nerts pile…time after time after time! We were amazed at how great a Nerts player he was, especially being a beginner. To say we are astonished would be an understatement. He soundly beat us every single game…and I made the comment, "Slow down, Mark. You're causing grandpa's brain to wear out."

With that statement, he revealed the fact that he had Jernigan blood flowing through his veins, saying, "What's wrong, grandpa? Are you getting too old to play?" He followed that by waving his hands up and down in front of my face, saying, "Slow down, grandpa! Slow down or you'll hurt your brain!" I was taken aback in shock and simultaneously proud and delightfully amused at his 7-year-old level of trash talk!

I said, "Let's go, boy!" and we began to count out our cards for our Nerts piles. As we counted together, I noticed he stopped at number 7 while I continued to count out 13 cards. I asked, "Why did you stop at 7? A Nerts pile has 13 cards, son."

He said, "My mom says I only have to have seven cards in my Nerts pile since I am only 7 and just learning to play the game."

My response: "You have mastered the game, son! Add six more cards to your pile." He whined, "That's not fair. I'm only 7."

I said, "It's more than fair. You're 7 and I have Parkinson's, so…keep counting!" I finally won a game…but he is 7 and fast and loves to beat grandpa and he proceeded to wear my brain down to the point of me just sitting there with a blank stare as I watched him tear through the game like he was amped up on speed!

It was after that legendary Nerts encounter that the family began to rate my level of well-being for any given day by asking me how many cards I have in my Nerts pile for the day. The more cards in my pile, the better day I am having. A 13-card day is primo, meaning I feel well enough to play a 7-year-old in a brisk game of Nerts. Any day I have less than seven cards in my Nerts pile means I am having a slow brain function day…and will probably not last long in a game of Nerts…or any other activity requiring brain power!

Speaking of less-than-seven-in-my-Nerts-pile moments, recently, at the local Starbucks drive thru, I was greeted by one of the young men who often serves me. He calls me by name and is always very kind. On the windowsill were two boxes for tips. "Buffy the Vampire Slayer" was written on one and "Supernatural" on the other, both shows from the early 90s. I laughed and said, "I've never seen either of those shows so I don't know where to tip.

He said, "You didn't watch those shows?! They were both very popular in the 90s!"

I replied, "I was busy making babies in the 90s, so I missed both of those shows." He laughed so hard at my response and pulled out another tip jar and said, "Here's a tip jar for guys like you!" He was still laughing as I drove away…and then it dawned on me what I had said. Who tells a person they barely know that they were busy making babies in the 90s?! A true Parkinson's moment!

I have a couple other Parkinson's moments involving Starbucks. On one occasion, I had just finished my workout and decided to treat myself to a skinny vanilla latte. I paid using a credit card and went about the rest of my day. That afternoon, I once again needed to use the credit card only to find it gone from its usual place in my wallet. Of course, my Parkinson's-weary mind went blank as I retraced my steps from the day. Melinda asked, "Where have you used the card today?"

I replied, "Starbucks and…and…Starbucks!"

Before I made the five-mile trip back to Starbucks, I called and asked if they had any credit cards left at the drive-thru that day. They responded with, "We actually have about 35 from the past two days. What's the name on your card?" I gave my name, and they found my card, but I wondered to myself, "Are there 34 other people with Parkinson's in the Starbucks drive-thru on any given day…or is that just an average of forgetful people around here?"

Since that day, I have twice nearly driven away without my card and a couple of times started to drive away without paying. Each of those times, I was stopped just before I made my getaway by the frantic window-server leaning their torso out of the drive-thru window, arms flailing, yelling, "Stop! You forgot your card… again!" or "Stop! You forgot to pay…again!"

Classic Parkinson's moments…

In less than four years as of this writing, I have already experienced enough Parkinson's moments to last a lifetime. While the struggle is real and there are periods of suffering, I honestly find it very helpful to laugh at my situation. I am in no way denying I do, indeed, have the malady and am in no way trying to belittle anyone who does not choose to see Parkinson's in the same way I do. Laughter really does work like medicine for my soul. It just does.

Sometimes I find it helpful to get a different perspective of my situation. One of the simple ways I accomplish this is to use positive terms for negative symptoms. Rather than seeing the symptoms as detrimental, I choose to call them the Perks of Parkinson's.

For instance, when I am having a particularly rough day dealing with the tremors in my right arm and hand, I give such episodes the title "The Trouble with Tremors." Why? Because of the original television series, *Star Trek*. If you recall episode 15 of the second season called "The Trouble with Tribbles," you will see that the Starship Enterprise visits a space station where they encounter small purring balls of fluff called Tribbles. Lt. Uhura brings one on board the Enterprise and the Tribble begins to multiply to such a degree that both the space station and Enterprise are overrun with the creatures. It is a funny episode that I still remember, and I was only seven years old at the time of its initial airing!

The trouble with Tribbles is that they continue to multiply even when steps are taken to alleviate their procreation. The trouble with tremors is that they tend to multiply the more I try to make them stop. I don't know why thinking of that *Star Trek* episode helps me during such moments, but it does, I suppose, simply because it brings a private giggle to my soul and takes my mind to a happy place.

Of course, there are other perks of PD that help lighten the burden. My wife is such a positive person; she immediately begins offering solace during intense moments of uncontrollable tremor by reminding me I have my own personal vibration device.

Tremors always make mealtimes more exciting. You have not lived until you are trying to get a forkful of food into your mouth while your hand is tremoring out of control. I can sense the entire gathering of family wondering if the food will actually make it to my mouth without flying from the fork or if I will notice them all trying to do so without me noticing. I notice...and it makes me laugh. I have learned to eat with my left hand for the more violent moments of mealtime tremors.

Another thing I have noticed is the tremors never appear when I want to intentionally show someone but miraculously appear whenever I hold hands with someone...like my grandchildren... who have been taught to refer to the tremoring hand as grandpa's Party Hand, signifying that grandpa is really, really excited to be with them.

I could not help but laugh at another recent mealtime prayer with our three-year-old grandson, Theo. Just as we were instructing the grandchildren to join hands for prayer, Theo requested that I sit beside him. I gladly obliged. He then proudly held up his hand and said with great confidence, "Look, grandpa! I have a party hand, too!" He then gave a perfect demonstration of a Parkinson's tremor. Needless to say, we adults snickered through the entire prayer...and I noticed several others mimicking Theo's interpretation of my party hand. Many are the perks of Parkinson's and many are the opportunities for Parkinson's moments. Don't worry. I have a few more to share.

ELEVEN
BELLING THE DAD

"A day without laughter is a day wasted."

— CHARLIE CHAPLIN

"A well-developed sense of humor is the pole that adds balance to your steps as you walk the tightrope of life."

— WILLIAM ARTHUR WARD

"Common sense and a sense of humor are the same thing, moving at different speeds. A sense of humor is just common sense, dancing."

— CLIVE JAMES

"The tragedy of life is not death but what we let die inside of us while we live."

— NORMAN COUSINS

e all die. I plan to die well despite my circumstances. Content. Joyful. At peace with the way I lived my life. Convinced of my family's love for me. Convinced of the reality of eternal life through faith in Jesus Christ, my Foundation, and knowing I am never alone, even through the process of dying. What difference does it make what eventually causes my death? I plan to die well by living well and enjoying the journey. Parkinson's will not have the last laugh. I will!

I have discovered that when I make light of my illness, people either respond with relief and are set at ease by my attitude or they respond with horror and find my attitude very discomfiting. My desire is to find joy along the PD journey. Some would call such a cavalier attitude a form of gallows humor.

Gallows humor is simply grim and ironic humor in a desperate or hopeless situation; humor that makes fun of a life-threatening, disastrous, or terrifying situation. That sums it up pretty well concerning my personal attitude. I mean no disrespect to anyone else suffering with PD. This is my personal experience and how I am choosing to live it.

My children tend to share my sense of humor. I make dad jokes without mercy and find even a stupid pun ingenious. My wife, on the other hand, takes everything literally — even a dad joke. I am Peter Quill — Star-Lord — to her Drax the Destroyer from Guardians of the Galaxy. Star-Lord takes very little seriously and tends to have a facetious wit. Drax the Destroyer takes everything literally.

As a case in point, there is a scene from Guardians of the Galaxy Vol. 1 in which Rocket the raccoon tells the other guardians to not speak in metaphors because metaphors will just go right over Drax's head. Drax responds, "Nothing goes over my head. My reflexes are too fast. I would catch it." That describes my wife. She is super smart and incredibly wise and is so trusting that she tends to take the words people say literally. Even the facetious kind...

My children are like Star-Lord. A conversation between Guardian Gamora and Star-Lord is a great example of how my children and I talk to one another.

Gamora: "It's dangerous and illegal work, suitable only for outlaws."

Star-Lord: "Well, I come from a planet of outlaws: Billy the Kid, Bonnie and Clyde, John Stamos."

And, if I may, I'd like to share one more example from Guardians of the Galaxy:

Star-Lord asks Gamora to dance.

Gamora: "I'm a warrior, an assassin. I don't dance."

Star-Lord: "Really, well on my planet, we have a legend about people like you. It's called Footloose."

Totally ridiculous and absurd but my kind of humor. I share this to relay a couple of conversations between my son Ezra and me that I thought were completely hilarious...but Melinda did not!

Melinda was talking with our son about how quiet I was around the house and how she sometimes worries about whether I am ok. She has a very real concern for my safety and wants to make sure I have not fallen somewhere and knocked myself unconscious. She also told my son that I am so quiet and that she is so focused on her work that I often startle her when I walk quietly into the room. In fact, I had just walked into our bedroom where Melinda was deeply focused on creating a very precise piece of jewelry and caused her to scream just a few seconds before Ezra walked into the room.

Ezra suggested to his mom that she should make a special bracelet with bells on it and secure it around my tremoring right wrist to always know where I might be. Instead of belling the cat, Ezra could help her bell the dad. This made me laugh until I had tears streaming down my face. It made Melinda very upset because she would never do anything to humiliate me like that. This only made us laugh more. I tried to explain to Melinda that it seemed practical to me and that it reminded me of the old fable called "Belling the Cat."

The fable concerns a group of mice who debate plans to nullify the threat of a marauding cat. One of them proposes placing a bell around its neck so that they are warned of its approach. The plan is applauded by the others until one mouse asks who will volunteer to place the bell on the cat. All of them make excuses. Ezra responded to his mom, "You make the bracelet and I'll put it on him."

Again, Melinda did not find it humorous at all. She found it quite insensitive. One of the most endearing things about my children toward me is that they feel confident enough in our love and relationship to tease me and, at times, mock me. Their facetious wit, when directed toward me, honestly makes me feel very loved. For Christmas that year, I bought a bracelet adorned with jingle bells, wrapped it, and had Ezra present it to me in front of Melinda. Ezra and I laughed hysterically...and Melinda surprised us with, "Ezra! That's so funny! You remembered!" Her excitement was genuine and her laughter healing. The only problem was that the bracelet was too small for my wrist.

Melinda said, "I can add elastic to it! We'll make it work! Great job, Ezra!" I didn't have the heart to tell her I had put Ezra up to it...which makes me giggle every time I think about it.

I must add that Melinda grew up in a home where she was belittled, teased and emotionally and verbally abused. A home where the abuse was masked in humor but meant to cut deeply. One way we deal with these two very different perspectives on facetious humor is that Melinda has the right to say, "That's enough," and we stop.

Recently, Ezra walked into our room while Melinda and I were watching a documentary series called "I Am a Killer" and I paused the show. Displayed across the screen was the title of this episode called "I Killed My Dad." His response? "I've been looking for different ideas and ways to do this. This show will be very helpful." Melinda was horrified. I again laughed until tears streamed down my face.

A few days later, he again walked into our room with a few wood chips he had picked up from a dead tree he is chopping down by hand. He thought we might enjoy the smell of the freshly hewn wood. Melinda loved the smell. I said, "I can't smell anything. I have little to no sense of smell."

Ezra said, "Interesting. Poison it is…" and he walked out of the room, me laughing, Melinda not. The thought of my son devising a plan to kill me and running with the joke for weeks on end just makes me giddy with anticipation and makes me chuckle to myself every time I even think about it.

Each morning, I have a regimen of vitamins and medicines I take. As a part of that daily routine, I must use a laxative to help keep my bowels healthy (bowel problems are yet another fun symptom of PD). Just as I began to stir the laxative in a glass of water one morning, Ezra walked by, saw what I was doing and asked, "How does that taste?"

I answered, "It doesn't really have a taste."

With a twinkle in his eye and a hint of sinister glee in his voice, he said, "Interesting," and just walked out of the house, leaving me in stitches and trying not to spew the contents of my mouth all over the kitchen!

Recently, Ezra was doing some work in the studio. I walked in and began to gasp for breath. The most horrid, acrid smell permeated the room. I asked, "What IS that?!" Ezra explained that he had taken his dog, June, for a walk that morning and June had come face to face with the business end of a skunk. After bathing June, the skunk stench was still very "there." Ezra thought it might be good to burn some small pieces of wood in the studio to rid the skunk's lingering essence. It only made it worse!

I said, while still gasping for my next breath, "Are you trying to kill me?"

Ezra's reply? "Thwarted again!"

Of course, I have proven Melinda and her concern for my

safety right on more than one occasion. I swim laps four days a week and tend to rise early to do so. Usually, Melinda is already up and at 'em, but one morning I could tell she was still in bed, sleeping away. I quietly made my way to my closet to put on my clothes for the drive to the swim center and did so without using even the light of my phone screen so as not to wake her.

For such mornings, I place my clothes on a small wooden chest in my closet for me to easily put them on in the dark. Of course, Parkinson's combined with total darkness caused me to become disoriented and I lost my balance. Luckily, I broke my fall with a face plant against the wall!

Miraculously, the thud of my head hitting the wall did not wake Melinda…but I immediately thought to myself, *Maybe belling the dad is not such a bad idea.*

TWELVE
SUGGESTIONS FROM MY CHILDREN

"It is more important to know what sort of person has a disease than to know what sort of disease a person has."

— HIPPOCRATES

"[My wife] and I choose to believe you don't have Parkinson's. You're just getting old."

— S.T., A SON-IN-LAW OF DENNIS JERNIGAN

"Don't tell mom."

— DENNIS JERNIGAN

have lost count of the times I have said, "Don't tell mom," to one of my children since my diagnosis. Melinda loves me and wants me on this earth-journey with her as long as possible. This tendency toward wanting me to stay around, of course, revolves around my health...and she is often concerned that I try things too daring for my age or for my condition. And, if I am being honest, she is right to be concerned!

A case in point: Recently, one of our granddaughters, a kindergartener, was set to march in a patriotic parade near the beginning of the new school year. Melinda was out of town helping another daughter prepare fall/Thanksgiving/Christmas home decorations and spending time with two of our grandsons. Melinda's last words to me were, "Please be careful," which, being translated, means, "Don't do something stupid!"

One of my sons told me he would ride to the parade route with me and meet my daughter's family and find seating for the parade. I noticed the streets had all been blocked and we were early enough to easily find perfect seating...and I also noticed something I had always wanted to try.

Parked on a nearby corner of the sidewalk in downtown Muskogee was a small group of self-propelled scooters...available to responsible adults...for a very affordable fee. Suddenly, the sun's rays caught a shiny portion of one of the chrome handlebars and I found myself in a road-to-Damascus moment. I was blinded by the beautiful light, yet I could not look away. As if it were calling my name, "Dennis...Oh, Dennis...give me a try," I found myself grasping those handlebars and pleading with my son, "How do I make this thing work? My precious..."

My son, who is all about exploiting my condition for his personal enjoyment, said, "Dad. You just download the app and pay for your time on the scooter and then park it anywhere on the sidewalk when you are done. Here. I'll just rent one for you." He was gleeful with anticipation of the possible outcome. You need to know that this particular son and I have an agreement. Any time I am doing something that could involve falling or bodily injury, he has the right to video the entire incident and laugh his butt off and then tend to my wounds...in that specific order!

He rented the scooter, showed me the controls...how to accelerate and how to stop...and I was ready! As I rode off down the empty parade

route, my last words were, "Don't tell mom!"

My son's next words were, "This might be the end of dad." I

felt both a thrill of exhilaration and a tinge of fear. Riding a scooter requires physical balance. Parkinson's affects my sense of physical balance. Are you getting why I felt both exhilaration and fear?

I made two trips up and down a city block without an incident. As I turned to head back down the still empty street, I said, "I'm starting the parade now!" and disappeared from the view of my family. To hear their concern and hear them question my sanity as I watched the video later literally made my day! I ended the ride... without incident or injury! Surprise!

After the parade, I told my son I wanted to spend some time riding scooters with him in the coming days. He suggested I start a scooter club for old guys. We then began brainstorming ideas for what we could call the scooter gang. Our final idea? The Super Silly Scooter Society (to be pronounced with a lisp...now say it again...it's ok to think this is funny). Since I had been in 4-H while growing up, I suggested that we could call the scooter club 4-S and that each 's' should stand for a specific set of character traits of 4-S members. Those traits? Stupid. Sassy. Sadly sweet. Supercilious (behaving or looking as though one thinks one is superior to others). The perfect combination of traits for an old-guy scooter gang. Need I say more?

Each year a local entrepreneur hosts a nationally recognized Renaissance Faire. For five weekends in May, just four miles from our home, 15,000+ people attend. Ezra and I attended and had a blast walking amidst the medieval setting, complete with a village, town crier, King and Queen, and various arts and crafts and myriad concessions. We thoroughly enjoyed talking with the huge number of appropriately dressed characters entertaining as they walked amongst the visitors.

One of my goals for the day was to enjoy a turkey leg. It was to be my main meal of the day. Ezra joined me in the quest to obtain this much-anticipated feast. We found a concession stand in the village selling turkey legs...at $18 a pop! But I had to have one...so I did...and so did Ezra!

We had just sat down at a picnic table and taken our first bites of delicious goodness when two very buxom ladies dressed in medieval garb that really brought attention to their cleavage sat down at the table with us. Ezra and I were somewhat surprised and said, "Hello!"

Speaking with very British accents, both ladies greeted us with, "Good day, fine sirs!"

Ezra and I were laughing and trying to keep our eyes focused on their faces when one of the ladies spoke to me, "I notice you handle your meat very well, sir!" I about spewed half-chewed turkey all over the place but managed to play into character with a bawdy comeback, saying, "Why, thank you, m'lady. There is a reason I happen to have nine children!" The ladies laughed and were very pleased their shocking statement had been received with such a response.

We then walked around some more until it was time for the main event: a falconry demonstration, followed by a dueling pair of swordsmen and, finally, the joust. Finding a prime spot near the top of the very steep bleachers, Ezra and I had such an amazing time commenting on certain characters and even interacting with some of them. It was so much fun being able to make comments under our breath about what we imagined each medieval character's motivation and home life might be like. It felt like I was on an episode of Seinfeld.

At the conclusion of the jousting event, we waited for the stands to clear out a bit before I attempted to make my way down. As soon as there was sufficient space to begin my descent, Ezra said, "Wait, Dad!"

I asked, "What's wrong?"

He said, "Nothing's wrong. I just want to video you coming down the bleachers in case you fall." It was in that moment that we actually made the following agreement: He has the right/duty to video me in any situation in case I fall or somehow find myself in an awkward predicament. In addition, he has the right/duty to laugh and comment upon the moment for posterity's sake, getting the entire event recorded for sharing with the family...and then, once that moment is sufficiently captured, to seek immediate medical help. This should explain a lot about my family!

It was actually Ezra who first coined "party hand" in reference to my tremors. One day as we joined hands to pray over a meal, he happened to be the one holding my right hand...and it began to quake quite vigorously. After the amen, he said, "Dad. It's like there's a party going on in your hand. It's your party hand!" And the name stuck!

Ezra has also made it one of his life goals to scare me whenever possible. Now that I think about it, one of his murder schemes may be to scare me to the point of inducing a heart attack. Hmmm. I should know better by now, but I do not think about looking around every corner whenever Ezra is in the vicinity. He pops out and I jump back and things I am carrying go flying. If I have water in my mouth, it goes spewing forth and, of course, Ezra has my permission to video the entire event.

As a result, we have an ongoing scare-the-crap-out-of-each-other feud going on even as I write this. After having been scared one too many times by my son, I recently caught a break. Actually, several breaks. One day, I was in the garage and noticed him walking toward the house. I quickly hid behind the door I knew he would enter. As he walked in, I simply stepped out and said, "Hello." He nearly fell to the floor as he stumbled backward in fright!

The very next day, I heard him coming down the stairs. I knew he would come through the kitchen, so I quickly ducked into the hallway. As he walked into the kitchen, I stepped out and said, "Hello."

Once again, he stumbled backward and said, "Good one, dad."

As if that weren't enough, the next day I was sitting in my car, in the garage, listening to the end of a podcast. In my rearview mirror I saw him headed home from the studio. I quickly turned off the engine...and waited. Just as he walked by my driver's side door, I opened the door and said, "Hello."

He stumbled back once again, but this time said, "Oh, now it's on, dad!"

I replied, "I'll be watching you...and waiting!" I felt that I had completely vanquished him. Man, was I wrong!

He waited a couple of days to plan his revenge, knowing that in my Parkinson's mind the feud was over and that I had won. Having finished my work for the day, I put on my pajama pants and tee shirt and settled into my recliner, heating pad on my tremoring right arm, and prepared to watch a documentary on American history. Then I received a text from Ezra.

"Are you going to get you and mom dinner?"

I replied, "No. She's cooking dinner right now. Why? Do you need me to go get you something to eat?"

He texted, "Yes, please! Could you get me a burger?"

My text back said, "Fries? Drink? What do you want on it?"

Ezra said, "Just a plain cheeseburger, fries, and a Dr. Pepper."

I responded, "Ok."

He replied, "Thank you so much! I'll CashApp mom."

I sent off a final text saying "Ok" and told Melinda I needed to help Ezra out since he was working through dinner. I made my way to the car, plugged in my phone, preparing to listen to a podcast, and backed out of the garage, my eyes fixed on the rearview mirror. Waiting for the right moment, Ezra jumped up from the cargo area in the back of my Kia Sportage and screamed, "Hello!" I pumped on the brakes, scared witless, one heartbeat away from cardiac arrest...and began laughing uncontrollably!

Hearing the screeching of brakes and my on-the-verge-of-tears laughter, Melinda came out of the house as I pulled back into the garage. When I explained to her what had just taken place, she began to laugh and congratulate Ezra on his victory. Ezra, still stuck in the cargo compartment, asked, "Dad, can you help me get out of here?"

I said, "I think I should just leave you there...but that was an awesome scare. Good one!" I hugged him and told him I loved him, and he went back to work.

While I was still chuckling and walking into the house, I

received his text that said, "There is more where that came from. This is only the beginning."

I texted right back, "It's on, my son…" Now I find myself plotting my revenge…while my son plots my demise, lol! I got him back the following morning. I heard his car door slam as he was about to enter the barn where we have the studio. Positioning myself next to the entrance, I flung my jacket in front of him and he stumbled backward saying, "I can't believe I fell for that. It's still on…"

My children find great pleasure in making me laugh, and to add to their pleasure, it is their goal to cause me to laugh whenever I am drinking something. I have literally spewed water on my computer screen, all over myself (and others in the vicinity), and out of my nose on more than one occasion. I never used to be that worried about spit takes, but Parkinson's has increased the odds greatly…and my quick-witted children have honed in on that fact!

One of my personal rules is that Dennis Jernigan does not get to call himself something his heavenly Father does not call him. That is a very steadfast rule in my life. A rule my children and wife hold me to. Over the most recent Christmas holiday, several of my children invited Melinda and me to join them in a session of the Smart Ass board game. It is a game of trivia.

After a slew of correct answers and getting close to winning the game, I missed an easy question and said out loud, "I am so stupid!" My children all replied at once, "Dad, you're the smartest person in the room, even with Parkinson's."

I said, "I know I am not stupid but that is how I felt."

My daughter promptly answered, "Dad, you're not stupid. You're just slow." We were all convulsing in laughter at this very true statement. PD does not make me stupid, but it does make me feel as if I am moving in slow motion at times! The statement came at just the perfect time and was delivered with such a keen wit that I felt very loved even when chiding myself for missing an easy answer.

My children are also very keen on suggestions to help me

through this phase of life. They have recommended I get a handi-capped sign from my doctor so I can get the best parking spots. While that makes me laugh, I honestly don't feel I am handicapped.

They also got me a tee shirt emblazoned with bold letters asking, "Do I have Parkinson's?" and below that question, two boxes. One is labeled "Yes" and the other "No." Between the boxes is a scribbled attempt at a check mark that misses both boxes and was clearly attempted by someone with severe tremors. I have never worn it publicly...but I giggle to myself every time I think about it!

Yet another of my children suggested I have business cards printed for use during foggy brain moments I experience in public like while checking out at Walmart or at the Chick-fil-A drive through. The card would include a brief explanation that I have Parkinson's along with my attempt at a signature which is, of course, illegible.

While my family continues to come up with suggestions for making my life easier and more joyous, I have thought of creating a tee shirt of my own design. The front of the shirt would include a warning sign followed by a list of symptoms those around me may observe:

This man has Parkinson's:

- May experience sudden glassy-eyed stare or momentary zombie-like symptoms.
- May have episodes of tremors and not the earthquake kind.
- Does not have a filter on what he says — he's just getting old and has Parkinson's.
- May burst into sudden fits of laughter and spew whatever beverage he happens to be drinking (this can come in handy when watering the flower garden).

The back of the shirt would have further warnings like:

- Do not allow this man to play on the slip-n-slide.
- Do not allow this man to serve carbonated beverages or open the beverage container he may be offering you. The caveat: to James Bond fans — DO allow him to shake your martini for you (even though he has never done so before). You will find him to be quite natural in a pinch.
- Do not allow this man to take part in any activity such as axe-throwing.
- May seem frozen in mid-sentence — just wait. He'll eventually get there.
- May forget why he has entered a room.
- May appear to be sad or angry or rudely bored. Again, just give him a couple of seconds and allow his system to reboot. He will eventually burst into laughter and appear to seem genuinely interested in what you have to say…even if he is not!

At Christmas gatherings we often surround the dining room table each night for board games. My favorites are word games like Balderdash and Wise and Otherwise. One night, my oldest son caught me doing something against the rules and said, "Dad, that's cheating!"

I didn't miss a beat, responding in the most pitiful voice, "Son, I have Parkinson's…" to which he replied, "So, we're playing the Parkinson's card now! Really?"

They have no mercy on me!

They have suggested other practical uses for me like, "His right hand makes for a great vibrator. He is great at keeping secrets. He is a great listener, great egg scrambler, great conversation subject, great for demonstrating jazz hands." You get the idea!

Most of all, my wife and children take great care of me and make me feel greatly respected and loved…and give me the freedom to laugh at myself. Here are some of the positive things they say about me:

"You will want him on your trivia team or to help with a crossword puzzle or Wordle or Jeopardy. He may forget his own name but can tell you the year the Magna Carta was signed and the location of Hadrian's wall as well as the lineup of the Knicks for the early 1970s era as well as the Milwaukee Bucks championship roster from the 1970s, and he can quote the entire lyrics from the song Wolverton Mountain from 1962 when he was only three years old."

What follows are some of the things my children have demonstrated to me along with some of the greatest and most cherished things my children have said to me since my diagnosis. Thinking about these spoken and demonstrated acts of love brings balance between the moments of suffering and moments of laughter for my soul:

"Dad appreciates life."

"Dad loves deeply."

"Deej is a legend."

"Dad is intensely nostalgic."

"Dad values others."

"Dad has steadfast faith in God."

"Dad loves and blesses those who hate and curse him."

"Dad loves his family."

"Dad adores mom."

"Dad is grateful for the lessons of Parkinson's and does not fear its worst."

"We love being around our dad."

"Papa J, you are a mountain of a man."

"Dad, thank you for letting me talk to you about anything. I wouldn't trade this year for anything."

"You're still dad. Nothing's changed."

"You could always get a job at a restaurant offering to shake salt or pepper on patrons' meals or salads…"

THIRTEEN
THE HEALING POWER OF GRANDCHILDREN

"The greatest legacy one can pass on to one's children and grand-children is not money or other material things accumulated in one's life, but rather a legacy of character and faith."

— BILLY GRAHAM

I recently had a conversation with one of my 8-year-old grandsons. He came over after school and I was reclining in my chair. When he finds me like that, he always sits right next to me in my chair, snuggling as close as he can get. I asked him how school had gone that day and if anything exciting had happened. He asked me questions in return, wanting to know how my day had gone. I told him, "My day was made perfect the moment you sat down beside me."

His next question caught me off guard and made me quite emotional. "What was your grandpa like?" he asked. I told him I had no memories of my grandpa Jernigan since he died when I was only 14 months old but that I felt very loved by him and that he was very proud of me.

My grandson asked, "How do you know that if you don't have any memories of him?" In that moment, I had the most tender feel-

87

ings of bittersweet joy flood through my entire being as I tried to explain to my own grandson why I loved my grandpa so much even though I had no memories of him. I told him I had been told stories about him and me by my grandma Jernigan as I grew older. Then I told him the stories.

"When I was a baby, my grandpa was in his late 60s and he worked as an oil and gas lease pumper or caretaker," I began. "His job was to go around to all the various oil and gas lease pumps in his area that covered parts of Okmulgee and Muskogee counties in northeastern Oklahoma and make sure all the pumps were working and that all the tanks were being tended to.

"Believe it or not, I began walking when I was only 8 months old. By the time I could sit up by myself, my grandpa would come and get me once or twice a week and take me with him to check on his pumps. There were no seat belts involved. No car seats. He just plopped me down next to him in the seat of his old pickup truck and went about his work. If someone else happened to be at one of the pump sites, my grandpa would take me out of the truck and walk up to the worker and tell him, 'Meet my grandson!'

"My grandma said he would show me off to anyone who would listen. She told me how he would pull his truck off the side of the road if he saw one of his friends working on a fence line and show me off…how he would run into town to fill up the gas tank on his pickup just so he could show me off to anyone he could. My grandpa loved me so much and was so proud to have me as his grandson that he would take me with him any time he could…just because he could. Even though I have no real memories of my grandpa Jernigan, I have a treasure trove of memories thanks to the stories my grandma told me about him. I will never forget him."

My grandson, sounding very wistful and mature beyond his years, then melted my heart beyond what I can adequately describe when he said, "I will never forget you, grandpa…"

No one wants to be forgotten but time has a way of making us feel we will one day be forgotten. Grandchildren have a way of making a grandparent — even one who is dying — feel they will be remembered forever. It is in the passing down of the love of a grandparent to the heart of a child that sees to it that, even though names may be relegated to a place on the family tree, the essence of who we are will never be forgotten.Our grandchildren and their simple approach to love and their genuine joy for life, mixed with their passion, creativity, and boundless imaginations, act as healing agents for my soul and body. I wrestle with them. Play hide and seek with them. Have indoor snowball fights with them (light, white, fluffy balls filled with foam and approved for indoor use by grandma!). Have grand adventures and scavenger/treasure hunts in the forest of Bren. Delight in taking them on fishing trips to the ponds even if all I do is go from child to child to help them untangle the amazing tangles they inevitably get their fishing lines into. Play the piano with them and sing with them. Play tic-tac-toe, Battleship, and Nerts until my brain becomes mush. Being with them does something to my soul only a grandchild can do. It is pure healing, restorative and genuine love and gratitude that they even exist and that I get to be even a short part of their lives.

I love conversations with my grandchildren and hearing their thoughts concerning the world. Several of my grandchildren, for some reason, consider and refer to adults as human and children something other than human. They cannot wait to grow up to be humans! They have an explanation for anything I might ask them. I learn so much about their home lives (more than their parents probably realize, lol!) through our conversations. One such example is a list of life rules my oldest grandson came up with when he was 4 years old. He had his mom make a video of him reciting his personal rules for life. They are as follows:

1. Be kind.
2. Tell a human (an adult).
3. Be kind again.
4. If you go somewhere, no chewing anything.
5. No picking (poking?) anybody's eyes.

6. Be kind to froggies.
7. If you're hurt, go tell a human.
8. If there's a fire ant, tell a human. Do not touch it.
9. Don't climb on the house.

Those are great rules that any person — human or otherwise — would find great practical benefit in knowing!

In September of 2022, I took three of my grandsons with me to trim branches and vines on one of the trails in the forest of Bren. My oldest grandson, 9 years old, was driving the John Deere Gator while the 7-year-old and the 5-year-old helped clear the fallen branches from the trail. I had the battery powered hedge trimmers lifted above my head as I trimmed some of the higher branches. Suddenly, I heard my grandson — the driver — yell, "No! Harry! Stop!"

The next thing I felt was the front left tire of the Gator rolling into and over my left leg. The weight and momentum of the Gator forced me to the ground, but the tire simply rolled over my leg and the Gator came to a stop without pinning me completely beneath it. This was one of those moments when I honestly wondered, *Is this the way I am going to die?*

I then thought, *I cannot die this way! My grandsons would never get over killing their grandfather, even if it was an accident...so I have to live.* Funny what you think about when you think you're about to die.

The surprise and the jolt of the impact left me lying on the ground, hedge trimmer clipping away near my face, and my grandsons gathered around me in fear. Cullen, the oldest, asked, "Ga Ga, are you ok?! Should I call someone for help?"

The fear and concern in his little voice melted my heart. I was so proud of him for the way he responded. He had immediately engaged the emergency brake and turned off the Gator and had run to my side. It took me several moments to respond due to the pain and shock I was experiencing. Ronald, the 7-year-old, asked, "Ga Ga! Are you ok?"

After a few moments, I said, "I am alright, boys. You don't need to call for help. I just need to lay here for a couple of minutes and then we can decide what to do."

Here's the picture. I have Parkinson's and have moments when life feels like it is in slow motion. I am working on a hillside trail in a very dense forest with a crew of three boys ages 5, 7, and 9. I have a hedge trimmer buzzing near my face while a large ATV rests mere inches away from where it ran me over and the three boys are being traumatized by the situation. This all happens within the span of a few seconds, but the moment feels as if it is taking place in super slow motion.

Finally feeling I had no major injuries and realizing I should probably do something about the hedge trimmer, I released the trigger and the buzzing stopped. Again, Cullen asked if I was ok and if he should call for help.

I said, "I am ok, boys. I am ok. Grandpa just needs to rest for a couple of minutes."

I then asked Cullen what had happened. He said, "Harry stepped on the pedal and made the Gator go. I didn't mean to run over you."

"I know you didn't, Cullen. It was not your fault." Turning to Harry, I asked, "Harry, is that true?"

His face was so guilt-ridden and sorrowful as he nodded.

We had a "come to Jesus moment" as I wanted to put the fear of God in him. All I asked was, "Harry, was that a wise choice you just made?"

He shook his head.

I then said, "Harry, unwise choices can hurt people. Your unwise choice could have hurt Ga Ga very badly." His little heart was so repentant. I hugged all the boys and suggested we choose to have a good day and finish the work despite what had just happened. I told them to get back on the horse and ride…and they treated me with kindness and responded with instant obedience the rest of the day. I chose to keep the incident between me and the boys to show them how to forgive and move on down the road.

Their parents are finding out as they read this. I count this as a bonding memory and a Parkinson's moment.

Another Parkinson's moment related to my grandsons involves one of their favorite activities: peeing off the side of the dock into the big pond! Sorry, ladies. It's just a guy thing. I remember being a boy and opening the hayloft door of our barn 12 feet above the ground with my brothers and cousins to see who could pee the farthest or having similar contests from a bridge high above a local creek. There is just something about peeing from 30 feet above the surface of the water that brings great delight and satisfaction to a boy (or to a 64-year-old man for that matter).

When my own sons, the twins, were 5 years old, we moved to our present home, which happens to be near two bridges over the local creek. I still remember the day I took them on an adventure, advising them, "Don't tell mom!" As we piled into my pickup truck, I said, "Come on, boys! Let's go on a guy adventure!" I'll never forget the absolute thrill on their faces as I lifted them onto the bridge railing and held them steady and told them to let 'er rip! They knew exactly what to do!

Back to my grandsons. Peeing off the dock into the pond is one of the most awesome and joyful things to witness because it just brings back so many wonderful memories (again, sorry, ladies…it really is a guy thing). Of course, they want to impress grandpa, so I feel so honored when they ask me to pee off the dock with them! This occurs only when the boys are together with me and their sisters are with grandma. Their comments make me laugh so much as they love to point out that they can pee farther than grandpa. I just tell them I could pee as far as they can when I was their age, which makes them giggle as they imagine me ever being a boy!

One day, I shared this story of how simple and fulfilling a pleasure I find in peeing off the dock with my grandsons with a close friend. The friend asked the obvious question: "What happens when you pee and your hand starts to tremor?"

I didn't miss a beat. "Remember the old Water Wiggle, that water toy from the 80s? It's like that!"

My friend burst out with a roaring laugh! A Water Wiggle was an outdoors toy that was nothing more than a plastic bulb-shaped object on a hose extension that attached to a garden hose. The extension would spray water into the bulb and allow it to fly around erratically. The friend said, "I can see it now! TMI!"

I assured him that I am always careful to use my non-trembling hand to commandeer my "hose" and that I have yet to shower my grandsons by using my right hand because I am ambidextrous, being able to pee with either hand! You may feel appalled that I would share such intimate details, but such simple things really do bring me great joy and help make memories that will last the lifetimes of me AND my grandsons. And I have Parkinson's, so I sometimes say what I'm thinking...out loud. "Did I just say that out loud?" Parkinson's...

I go out of my way to encourage my grandchildren to seek Jesus and to walk in faith. How? Just being like Jesus to them and by teaching them to see even harsh realities of life from a positive, God-centered point of view. I write them stories and I write them songs and I sing to them at bedtime whenever they spend the night with us...just as I used to do for their parents. One of my favorite things to hear at bedtime is when a grandchild asks, "Can you sing me one of the songs you used to sing to my mommy/daddy when they were little?" I LIVE for such moments.

Talking about my grandchildren brings me so much joy even in the midst of the journey through Parkinson's, but I must say, hearing their thoughts and comments on life keep my joy constantly overflowing the reservoir of my heart. Here are a few random comments from my grandchildren through the years.

A 3-year-old grandson whispered into his dad's ear, "Can you count my hair?"

A 4-year-old granddaughter said, "Cousins ruin everything."

"Ga Ga. I want you and grandma to live in the house next door to our house." I replied, "I would like to do that, but someone else lives there." Their 6-year-old response? "We could just kill them, and you could move in." Ah, the logic of children. Welcome to my world!

Another granddaughter arranged her own wedding ceremony in first grade and held said ceremony at recess one day. The groom wore a tie. The bride wore a gown-like dress. There were groomsmen and bridesmaids and someone to perform the ceremony. I was, at once, appalled and proud of her organizational skills and passion!

All the girls want to marry their male cousins. I gave up trying to explain why that cannot happen but realize they will one day get it! All my granddaughters think their male cousins are very handsome.

One set of four siblings calls TV trays baby tables.

Another set of boys calls sweatpants long sleeve pants.

A 3-year-old grandson saw someone walking in their neighborhood while smoking a cigarette. His interpretation? "Mom, that guy has an air blow thing."

My firstborn grandchild, a grandson, called me Ga Ga from the get-go and that was the first word he said. Not Da Da or Mama! Some of the children call me Ga Ga. Some call me G Pa. Some call me grandpa. One calls me gramps. I gladly answer to all of them.

One of my Aussie granddaughters, 5 years old at the time, demonstrated how to solve a Rubik's Cube. I love this quote. "You twist it and make the colors go to the same spot. It may be a very long time. I haven't done this before."

One of my grandsons takes great delight in scaring me and how I respond with Parkinson's! His tactics are very much premeditated and performed with stealth, and I always jump and scream! I think he gets it from uncle Ezra…

Our 4-year-old granddaughter refers to butter knives as baby cutters.

Another granddaughter said recently with great passion, "[Brother], you've gotta come smell this! It's so good! Mmmm. Mmmm. I could smell this all day!"

A 7-year-old granddaughter recently sent a video with a food-tasting demonstration she and her sister were conducting. "We are going to try star fruit. 3-2-1, go. It's sweet like candy and tastes like candy…and then it has the flavor of poison. Well, a flavor of leaf. Yeah, at the end, it's an aftertaste. A disgusting aftertaste." I appreciate her creative description but wonder how she might know the flavor of poison. Makes me wonder if she, too, is working with my son, Ezra, as an accomplice to my murder.

When Cullen was 9, he asked what types of restaurants I and grandma liked. He mentioned a couple and I told him grandma does not like either of those because she does not like buffets. The fact that food is out in the open and "protected" by a sneeze bar explains her reasoning. Cullen, in retelling this story to his mom, said, "I find it so weird that grandma is the only one who doesn't like buffets, but she likes coffee. It's just so weird to me." A complete non sequitur, which makes complete sense to my Parkinson's brain! (A non sequitur is a conclusion or statement that does not logically follow from the previous argument or statement. Something grandchildren are experts in.)

Remember how I began this chapter — talking about how I had no real memories of my own grandfather and how no one wants to be forgotten? I recently got a precious glimpse into the practical, simple way a grandchild sees to it that their grandparents will never be forgotten.

My grandson, Theo, just turned 4. We attended his birthday party in Joplin, Missouri, at one of those indoor playgrounds, replete with a massive ball pit (children's germ bath), four levels of tunnels, nooks and crannies, and many, MANY slides. Theo enjoyed getting me into the ball pit and piling hundreds of balls on top of me until he could no longer see me. I would rise up like a monster and scare him and he would squeal with glee and say, "Again, grandpa monster!" And I would oblige.

His little brother, 2-year-old, Edison, wanted to go down the slides with me so we headed to the toddler-sized slides. Little did I know, but he had his eye set on conquering the big-boy slides. You know. The ones that began their descent from the fourth level. He looked forlornly at me and said, "Ga Ga! Slide," as he pointed toward the Mount Everest of slides.

It only took us 10 minutes or so to make our way through the four levels of maze-like tunnels, but we finally arrived. Edison was ready to go but did not want to go down by himself. I, on the other hand, needed to sit down and catch my breath. After a couple of minutes, I sat down in one of the four side-by-side slides and said, "Ok, Edison. Let's slide. Sit here on grandpa's lap and we'll go down together."

He said, "No. Slide," as he sat down in the slide next to me, took my hand, and shoved off!

He was ecstatic. I am positive that, to him, it felt like he HAD conquered Mount Everest. His response? "Again, Ga Ga! Again!" And, of course, I obliged...for at least five trips before I finally had to say to him, "Edison, Ga Ga is done." His dad took over slide duties from that point.

My point?

Several weeks later, Edison's mom, my daughter, Raina (who was 8 months pregnant with our 13th grandchild at the time — a granddaughter), Face Timed me and said, "Edison wants to show you something."

I asked Edison to show me. He then laid his head on his mommy's belly and spoke to his unborn sister, "Ga Ga! Slide! Ga Ga Slide!" He wanted his baby sister to have something to look forward to...as if he wanted her to know me already!

Raina told me he had done that several times and that he wanted to call me and show me himself. I could hardly speak I felt so loved...and then I remembered my own grandpa that I had no real memories of and I had my mind opened up to the vast genera-tion upon generation of grandparents passing down the deepest kind of love to the next generation. I knew I would never be forgotten even if my name was. And that brought a depth of healing to my Parkinson's-addled mind. I felt, well, restored. Grandchildren simply love us and that is enough.

My favorite quote from one of my grandsons says it all as I try to explain the healing, restorative power of the love of a grand-child. "When Grandpa says hi to you in the morning, it always brings you joy, doesn't it? I'm always happy to see him."

If that was all I got from my grandchildren, that would be enough. Honestly, PD or not, I feel like the most blessed man on earth. Our grandchildren are a much-needed balm for my soul.

"I know I will leave my work unfinished. I just hope I planted enough seeds in my children and grandchildren that they will continue."

— DAVID ROBINSON

FOURTEEN
INTIMACY (WE'LL GET THROUGH THIS)

"Love cures people — both the ones who give it and the ones who receive it."

— KARL A. MENNINGER

A little over a year after we had received the official diagnosis of PD, Melinda and I had been roughed up quite a bit in the way it affected and disrupted our lives. Due to the nature of the illness, I had to become even more disciplined than I had been before the diagnosis, and I was a pretty disciplined guy.

I ran three miles a day. I mowed our tremendously large lawn each week (takes about two hours using a zero-radius turning mower with a 60-inch mowing bed). I mowed and maintained a two-mile trail system in the magical forest Melinda and I created for our grandchildren. I wrote music weekly. I wrote a week's worth of daily devotions each week (I have written, as of this writing, over 12 years/books worth of devotional thoughts). I answered dozens of emails requesting spiritual wisdom regarding people's need for understanding their identity in Christ. I traveled all over the world sharing my music and testimony in ministry, averaging three engagements a month. I led a home church group each Wednesday evening. I spent one on one time with our children as much as possible. I lived life out loud...until I couldn't.

When my health became an issue and we knew it was something severe affecting my body, everything changed in an instant. I wrote Melinda this letter during that period in our lives:

April 21, 2020

We'll Get Through This

I know it can't be easy for you as it relates to Parkinson's and what it is doing to my body and mind. I recognize the feeling of helplessness I sometimes sense you are feeling...and I understand that...and I hate that for you. That being said, here is what I purpose to do for you...

I will try to be better at intimacy with you...whether we have physical intimacy or not. I know you need me to touch you more...to be a better listener...to hold you for no reason other than you need to be held...to enjoy watching you be the best mom ever to our children and to enjoy watching you be the most awesome grandmother to our grandchildren.

I want to dream with you about our future...I want our legacy to be one of the most amazing love stories ever lived out in real life...and I will not allow Parkinson's to dictate that in any way.

I will listen even when my mind feels overwhelmed.

I will touch you even when I feel too weak to reach out.

I will hold you even when I feel less than capable to meet your needs.

I want to sit on the porch with you and watch our grandchildren play...or watch the sun go down...or watch a thunderstorm like a grand fireworks display put on by God just for us...or worship Jesus with you on Wednesday evenings - even if it's just me and you...actually, especially when it's just me and you.

I know I have periods where my mind seems to shut down...but I'm still in there...still wanting to communicate with you...but not always able to get my words out. When I go silent, please remember that and know that my greatest desire is to see you happy and fulfilled...and that you feel loved and taken care of.

One of my favorite things to do is to brag on you. I am so proud to tell other people how great a woman...how great a wife...how great a mother...how great a grandmother...how great and amazing you are at creating things of beauty...how you are not afraid to figure things out that I have no clue about...how grateful I feel to have married someone so out of my league by leaps and bounds. I am so proud of you...

I will not allow Parkinson's to dictate my love for you. When we face issues brought about by the disease, I will do my best to see those issues from God's perspective and work it out from His point of view. Above all, I will not allow the enemy to cause division or separation of any kind.

I want to be your hero...your knight in shining armor...your lover... your champion...your best friend...but feel incapacitated at times. What I choose to see when those moments come up are the little ways I can still be those things for you...like going to get us lunch...like going to get us a treat from Braum's...like picking up piles of sticks and taking them to the burn pile even though it wears me out...like being there for our children and grandchildren even if I don't have much energy beyond just sitting there being with everyone.

I would feel lost without you...and I am trying to learn to be content with just being and not feeling like I have to always be doing something to feel valued. I feel like I am having to learn who I am all over again...every day...

I just want you to know how grateful I am to have you to go with me through these new and uncharted waters we are facing. I need you to know that and to know I love you beyond whatever life throws our way. Like you said: we will get through this...

I love you...

DJ

FIFTEEN
LOSING ONE'S MIND WITH GRACE

"I think I am losing my mind, but nobody can tell the difference."

— ANONYMOUS

According to the Alzheimer's Association website, alz.org, Parkinson's disease dementia is a decline in thinking and reasoning skills that develops in some people living with Parkinson's at least a year after diagnosis. The brain changes caused by Parkinson's disease begin in a region that plays a key role in movement, leading to early symptoms that include tremors and shakiness, muscle stiffness, a shuffling step, stooped posture, difficulty initiating movement and lack of facial expression. As brain changes caused by Parkinson's gradually spread, the person may also experience changes in mental functions, including memory and the ability to pay attention, make sound judgments and plan the steps needed to complete a task. Because Parkinson's disease and Parkinson's disease dementia damage and destroy brain cells, both disorders worsen over time. Their speed of progression can vary widely.

I know PD will eventually affect my mind. It is a degenerative

disease, meaning it is characterized by progressive, often irreversible deterioration, and loss of function, especially relating to
my ability to move and in my brain's ability to process information
somewhat rationally. In the case of PD, my movement and brain
function are slowly (at least it feels that way to me) deteriorating.
The physical symptoms are the most apparent at this point. Others
may argue the mental symptoms are leading the way and have
been for a long time! Certain things that occur in my life tend to
leave me riding the fence as to whether my brain function is
normal or if I am experiencing diminishing brain function. Here
are a few examples.

Melinda and I are so opposite in myriad ways. She's a woman.
I am a man. She is an extrovert. I am an introvert. She is bluntly
honest. I avoid confrontation. She sees the world in black and
white. I see it in grey and vivid technicolor (just humor me...I have
Parkinson's). She does not suffer fools. I am a fool she promised to
suffer in our wedding vows (a fool in the sense that I love a wry
and silly sense of humor and foolishly go out of my way to come
up with a good dad joke). She loves Hallmark and Lifetime
movies. I would rather face a firing squad. She speaks her mind. I
am overtly diplomatic. She reads music like a pro. I play by ear.
She is super girly and lives for accessorizing and tea parties with
our granddaughters and I enjoy rough housing with our grandsons all over the floor until I become an exhausted, sweaty, immov-
able blob of a grandpa at the bottom of the boy pile. My point is,
being married to one another has caused us to see marriage as an
intricate dance because we see life so differently from one another.

Knowing Melinda is like trying to solve the greatest mystery of
the universe while dancing to the most romantic music the human
soul can muster, all while trying to avoid stepping on her feet...

In college, I would sneak away from the Baptist university I
attended once a month to attend a dance at the nearby Catholic
college. We could not use the word "dance" on campus, so we
called this monthly dance-a-thon a "function." I was the guy who

was raised with African American friends who taught me how to dance. This served me well in college.

Yes, I was the guy at the function who, once the music started ramping up, went into a zone. I became the guy all the girls wanted to dance with because I was so uninhibited (hard to believe, but true) and fun. On more than one occasion, my friend and one of Melinda's roommates, JR, and I would be going at it so intensely — Saturday Night Fever style — that the dancers would clear the dance floor around us as people moved out of our way to let us freestyle.

I don't dance much anymore...except with my wife. We have very intimate moments when we are all alone and I put on two of our favorite slow dance songs, both by Ed Sheeran: "Perfect" and "Thinking Out Loud." These are moments of purest ecstasy and are like a healing balm for my soul. If I were to continue describing our slow dance times, this would be the time where you say with disgust (and a tinge of jealousy), "You two need to get a room!"

Dancing with Melinda is such a blessing to me, but to be honest, the dance gets quite confusing for me sometimes...like when she is needing to talk about her day.

In his article, "A Willingness to Communicate," online at drjamesdobson.org, respected founder of Focus on the Family, Dr. James Dobson, says a woman needs to say as many as 50,000 words in a day while a man needs to say about 25,000. By the time a man gets through with his day, he has used most of his words. A woman has not! This seems very reasonable and true to Melinda and me!

Throughout the course of our (so far) 39 years of marriage, we have danced the dance of communication fairly well. I have learned to let her talk and have refined the skill of knowing when to interject an occasional, "Is that right?" or "Oh, I'm so sorry" or "Mmm-hmm."

We perform this part of the dance very well. She gets to share her emotions in words and I listen...until I don't. I know the you-know-what has hit the fan when she suddenly asks, "Are you even listening to me?" My pre-planned "Of course I am listening" falls apart the moment she asks the dreaded question, "What did I just say?!" Major step-on-foot-of-my-dance-partner moment.

Through such moments, I really have gotten better at listening, but in all fairness, her ability to talk about three or four different subjects at the same time tends to confuse the heck out of me. One second, she's talking about a conversation she had with her friend Twyla and the next she is talking with me about a jewelry design she has just come up with and then is on to how the children are doing and what cuteness came forth from one of our 13 incredible and amazing grandchildren today...and is suddenly asking me my opinion.

I responded to the last reasonable thing that came out of our conversation with, "I don't think our 3-year-old grandson should be punished for saying the word "poop."

She replied, "What are you talking about?! I asked you what you think of these new pink earrings! You aren't even listening to me!"

I then calmly went through the lineup of conversation topics in the order I received them, resting the defense's case with the concrete fact that her last comment to me was about our grand-children.

Her response: "But I was asking you about the earrings!"

I once again went through the conversation in proper sequence and asked, "How was I supposed to know you were asking about the earrings?"

Her very sincere response? "You're just supposed to know."

At that moment, I realized either I'd had Parkinson's for the last 39 years or I have a much longer dance to go in the journey of unraveling the mystery of who Melinda is than I realized!

Recently, Melinda was working on her phone, doing a bit of marketing, and asked me to be quiet so she could select music for a post about her latest jewelry piece. She then said, "Ok, I am done."

I started watching some dad joke videos on my phone and she said, "I told you I needed you to be quiet."

I asked, perhaps foolishly, "Why? You said you were done."

She said, "Because I'm not done."

How would you interpret that? I have Parkinson's but…

Melinda has a way of making me laugh that no one else can duplicate. She just lives her life honestly and literally and rolls her eyes at my dad jokes, which only makes me laugh even more. Yet, there are many more occasions when she does something so unexpected that it catches me off guard and makes me laugh uncontrollably.

As an example, we were getting ready for bed recently. Melinda always uses a nasal spray just before bedtime. She had worked very intensely on her jewelry all day and we had received news that a close family friend had been rushed by ambulance to the hospital, so her mind was being pulled in many different directions as we prepared for sleep. Melinda grabbed her nasal spray and, rather than spraying it into her nostrils, sprayed the mist into her mouth. She began choking and laughing and I asked her why she was laughing. She said, "I just sprayed nasal spray in my mouth." I snorted in laughter, and we got so tickled we could not stop giggling.

After we settled down a bit, she kissed me goodnight and I said, "Wow! That makes my mouth feel so clear and uncongested." Once again, we began to giggle uncontrollably. As we were still laughing about that, I got a text with the friend's health update and I was trying to read it to Melinda while trying to suppress my giggles. As I attempted to read this very serious text, I sucked in my stomach so as to gain control…and my shorts fell down around my ankles, leaving me completely naked. Thank God none of the grandchildren were spending the night that evening! When that happened, our laughter turned to sheer convulsion and we gave up trying to stop giggling. I slept well that night!

Back to my son Ezra and his way of making me feel loved in the midst of Parkinson's (death threats aside), in October of 2022 he asked me if I would be offended if he went as me for Halloween. He explained the costume would consist of him walking around with a tremor in his right arm. I told him that would be fine and that I would not be offended. After thinking about it a bit more, he thought it would offend other people, though, so he went as something else. For some reason, it just makes me happy that he would even think of such a costume.

Why do I share such stories with you? Because life is full of moments when we wonder if we are losing our minds. Some are funny moments. Some not so much. I know PD affects my mind... my brain...but I have to be vigilant in renewing my mind and choosing right thoughts despite moments that make me think I might be losing it, whether silly or serious.

I often questioned my sanity long before I was ever diagnosed with PD. On more occasions than I care to count, I have been told I have lost my mind concerning certain controversial matters. During such times, I have often felt overwhelmed by the world's point of view to the point of questioning my own sanity. Call me crazy and call me demented, but I have a choice as to what I think, and I recognize there may come a day when, due to my age or PD or a combination of both, when I lose control of my thoughts. I am taking steps to counter such a day.

I continue to realize the importance of renewing my mind by speaking and choosing to believe God's Word about me. I have shared some humorous memories that remind me life, even in its harshest times, can be seen from a joyful point of view. This helps keep my mind healthy. Until the day I die, I will continue to practice renewing my mind.

Here are a few examples of some of the thoughts PD has brought about and how I have chosen to view them:

There are times when I find myself thinking Melinda does not find me attractive anymore. The truth: she tells me daily she is on my team, that we are in this together and that she will give her physical love to me any time I need it. She calls me her man and calls me big daddy and she makes me feel like a man.

There are times when I find myself thinking she needs me to die at a certain age to be best positioned financially for her future. The truth: as a man, I see myself as her provider and will continue to fulfill that role as long as I have breath and capability. She wants us to grow old together. We are getting ready to purchase cemetery plots and are taking legal steps to make our final days a blessing and not a burden to our children. This is what a responsible man does…but I plan on being around as long as I can!

There are times when I find myself thinking people are judging me due to my tremors or facial expression or slowed or slurred speech. The truth: some are. Most don't. Either way, I am still here and still planning on living the most joyful life possible, PD be damned!

> And do not be conformed to this world, but be transformed by the renewing of your mind, so that you may prove what the will of God is, that which is good and acceptable and perfect.
>
> — ROMANS 12:2 NASB

I cherish the funny moments of life and, at the same time, I have found maturity to keep on living by receiving God's grace during the trying times. This has been accomplished by constantly renewing my mind.

One of the practical ways I am renewing my mind is by refusing to be an angry, selfish man should dementia be a part of my journey. I plan on being kind in my old age, even if I lose my mind. Something that gives me great joy in making such a statement is that I am programming my mind now for losing it later. Seriously.

If I should lose my mind, I want my children and grandchildren to find such joy in talking with me in that state of mind that they fill the treasure troves of their memories of me with funny things I say or do, be it spraying nasal spray in my mouth or be it losing my shorts and mooning the world. I am counting on the grace of God to fill even the mindless ramblings of an old man with such deep joy that I step out of this life into the next with laughter...leaving a legacy of the laughter of a family who dearly loves me and entering into the laughter of a Father God who is so glad I am home He can't help but laugh!

SIXTEEN
DEALING WITH PRIDE

"Pride makes us artificial and humility makes us real."

— THOMAS MERTON

"There are two kinds of pride, both good and bad. 'Good pride' represents our dignity and self-respect. 'Bad pride' is the deadly sin of superiority that reeks of conceit and arrogance." — John C. Maxwell

One of my inner circle friends I have known since college days, Reggie, and his wife came to spend a few days with Melinda and me. They live in Florida. We live in Oklahoma. The plan was to spend a lot of time together Sunday through Tuesday. I dutifully saved up my strength for the visit and promptly used it all up on the first day. It was such a blessing to be with them and I felt so special that they would come so far to visit me that I took part in every activity and conversation with everything I had in me. The next day, I was in what I refer to as my zombie state…or walking comatose state.

Our plan for their last night in town was to enjoy a nice dinner together at a local restaurant. The evening began so well. I even began to feel a bit revived from my zombieness. After the hostess seated us, our waitress introduced herself and nervously asked us to be patient with her as she was still a trainee at her position and that this was her first night to work alone. Wanting to ease her apprehensions, I said, "That's perfect because we are all in training as diners, so we should be fine!" Everyone laughed and I felt invigorated. For a moment. It seemed that the effort it took to make one simple joke had sapped me of my energy and I, once again, found myself feeling that now all-too-familiar zombie feeling of the walking dead.

This means my brain felt foggy and that I found my mouth not speaking the words my brain was telling it to speak, making for many awkward moments during our meal. My face was in full mask mode made obvious by the blank stare and emotionless expression. When the conversation grew awkward or even silent, I felt compelled to apologize. Each time, our dear friends assured me there was no need to apologize. It had become too much for me by the time we ended our dinner.

I felt I had let them down, that I had let my wife down, and that I had ruined what should have been a more festive evening. I honestly felt deeply embarrassed. As we walked to the car to head home from the restaurant, I once again apologized and, again, they told me to stop with the apologies. I said, "I feel like the party pooper."

Reggie grabbed me in a big bear hug and whispered into my ear, "If you're the party pooper, I'll be your toilet paper." His willingness to step into my moment of distress in such a humorous and outrageous way was so disarming and love-filled that it reduced me to tears and laughter...and caused me to recognize something major had just taken place.

My response to Reggie? "You may be a redneck..."

Even though the symptoms of PD are oftentimes on full display and though one may feel I have a very valid reason to be embarrassed, the truth is that my feelings of inadequacy actually pinpoint the root of those feelings. Reality is that, even with PD, I can choose how I will respond to those symptoms. Every feeling can be traced to a thought we are thinking. When I care more about what people think of me than I care about enjoying their company, I am walking in pride.

When I stepped back from the events of the evening and gave an honest look at my responses, I became painfully aware that my energy had been sapped by trying to maintain and control what I perceived others were thinking of me. As soon as Reggie whispered those precious words into my ear, my pride was revealed and I was instantly humbled and set at ease. And I felt a tinge of clear-headedness return. I felt so absolutely loved. Humility does a mind good.

Humility is a modest or low view of one's own importance. Reality is that I am not here to be served, but to serve. Reality is that I am not here for my own glory, but for God's. Reality is that God wastes nothing. Not even PD. Reality is that self-pity and pride do not look good on me. Reality is that caring for others despite my own needs looks really good on me. Humility looks good on me regardless of my circumstances.

> For through the grace given to me I say to everyone among you not to think more highly of himself than he ought to think; but to think so as to have sound judgment, as God has allotted to each a measure of faith.
>
> — ROMANS 12:3 NASB

> Humble yourselves in the presence of the Lord, and He will exalt you.
>
> — JAMES 4:10 NASB

Pride is having an excessively high opinion of oneself or one's importance. When my focus is on me and on what others think of me, I open my mind up to self-pity and worry about whether I measure up. Arrogance and self-importance tend to make me look silly, selfish, self-satisfied, and smug. No one looks good clothed in pride. Pride always leads to loneliness and leaves much emotional wreckage in its path. Let's be honest: No one likes to be around arrogant and prideful people because such attitudes tend to make those around them feel unimportant and inferior.

Pride [goes] before destruction, And a haughty spirit before stumbling.

— PROVERBS 16:18 NASB

For years, especially before I hit my late 50s, I felt somewhat invincible. My attitude was, at times, "Don't tell me I can't accomplish something. I'll do it just to prove you wrong." Men tend to have a Super Man attitude and a Super Man ego to go with it, often leading to prideful arrogance. Parkinson's became like Kryptonite to my Super Man attitude, but humility became my remedy and the balm for my wounded soul.

After Parkinson's (APD), I could no longer mow the entire lawn. To do so left me physically and mentally drained for several days. I took great pride in keeping not only the lawn mowed but in keeping the front of our property neat and well-groomed. It crushed me the day Melinda hired a crew of professional lawn mowers to take over the lawn. How did I deal with this crushing blow? I humbled myself and accepted the help. Humility required me to get honest about my weakening body and accept the reality that doing so in no way diminishes who I am as a man. Humility requires that I recognize the season of life I am in and prepare the way for those who follow me by simply being there for them. That is enough.

Now, I can at least keep the area around the big fishing pond mowed since it takes only about 30 minutes and I only have to do it every other week. In addition, I mow the forest trails for the grandchildren. This takes a couple of hours, but I only must do it three to four times a year and I am deeply motivated to keep up with both the pond and the forest by imagining the fun they provide for my grandchildren. After pond and forest mowing day, I am toast for about two days. But it's worth it.

Manly pride, what I call "the blessed curse of virility," has been assaulted by PD in a life-altering way. I always considered myself sufficiently virile, having been blessed with stamina, strength, energy, and a strong sex drive and the ability to thrive on only five hours of sleep a night. I took great pride in this until PD changed my definition of virility. Now I see virility as God's strength in me to walk in humility regardless of my physical well-being and seeing my life and identity as a man from God's point of view. Though I am physically weak, I am strong in the grace of God. Though I may be weak on the physical battlefield, I am strong in the true battleground of every man: the mind. I am strong when I remind myself I have been given the mind of Christ. From my point of view, the strongest man's man I know is the man who bows his masculinity in humility and service to God and others.

Since the late 1980s, I have lived a very public life due to my personal testimony of faith in Christ and the music God has poured into my life. Having a very public ministry brought with it a measure of influence and fame (or infamy, depending on what you think of my testimony!). Surprisingly, that public role, both in concert and speaking engagements, has been one of the easiest things to give up. PD made me realize I needed to take a step away from public travel and simply give myself permission to rest. What I have discovered is that I can still affect the world via social media and the many years' worth of songs and books I have yet to release. I can continue to touch the world long after I am gone!

The most difficult things I had to receive grace for in order to walk in humility were quite simply the things that brought me some of the greatest joy in my life. PD greatly diminished my vocal abilities. I am not defined by how well I sing or even if I CAN sing. PD greatly affected my abilities at the piano due not just to the near-constant tremors but in using the three right-most fingers of my right hand. After only a few minutes of playing the piano, these fingers become useless and I have to mentally compensate using only my thumb and pointer finger. I am not defined by how well I play the piano.

Perhaps the biggest blow PD has gut-punched my pride and ego with is the neurological effects on my sense of rhythm. I used to be able to play any song in any key at any time, adapting to any rhythm simultaneously. I was always able to play a song while talking to an audience due to the way music came so naturally to me. Now it is a mental chore for me to maintain an even tempo and a mental drain to try and navigate the cognitive minefield syncopated rhythms have become. Humility brings me back to earth as I recognize nobody cares about those things in the vast scheme of the universe. Those rhythmic abilities or lack thereof don't define me.

I used to take pride in being romantically expressive to my wife, finding it very natural to reach out and touch her during various moments of the day or to leave her little love notes reminding her of how much I love her and desire her. PD has seen to it that those once-natural things I did not even have to think about have become overshadowed by a mental fog that seems to delight in clouding that romantic expression. I have to be intentional to do those things now…and it makes me sad to think my wife might ever feel neglected or might think I no longer find her desirable. Pride comes when I consider those things might mean I am less than a real man. Humility is laying down my life for my wife despite the mental fog. My wife is faithful to remind me how much of a man I am to her. Her love for me is truly humbling.

I used to take pride in keeping up with my children even after they left home and became adults. PD has made wanting to be constantly available to my children unrealistic. As a dad, I have to let them go and let them find their own way through life. I am available if they need me, but not defined by whether they ever seek my counsel or blessing or spend time with me. We are joined at the heart. Bottom line.

There were other pride-crushing moments to follow, but these were good kinds of crushing. I had to admit I needed help in cleaning the gutter near our pool periodically and found joy in asking grandchildren for assistance and great elation in watching them bless me with their helpful attitudes and youthful ability to bend down to clean the gutters in half the time it would have taken me. I absolutely love the sense of accomplishment that washes across their faces upon the completion of the task (plus, the possibility of receiving a couple of dollars from grandpa doesn't hurt, lol).

Inviting my children and grandchildren into my life by simply humbling myself and asking for help has brought such a warm and deep richness to our relationships. There is a time to do for one's self, but there comes a time when asking for help is the place of true strength.

My grandchildren now know how to vacuum the pool for me. That was an easy ask because that means they get to put the vacuuming robot we affectionately call R2 D2 into the pool after cleaning the debris from the robot's filter basket.

I had always dreamed of being the energetic grandpa who had boundless energy to play with his grandchildren. PD has robbed me of that kind of stamina. Humility allows me the freedom to simply be satisfied by being in their presence. Even with PD I can lie down on the floor and let them wrestle with me, which is another way of saying, "It's fun piling on top of grandpa!" My grandchildren make me feel special and needed because that is how I work to make them feel — despite PD — and that is enough for me.

Life is not about me. Life is about God and others. Blessing the next generation. Blessing those who came before me. We all die. I choose to die well…saturating my mind with humility despite the state of my health. This brings healing to my often-foggy soul.

PD has brought a level of humility I think has been healing for me. Pride just doesn't look good on me. Performing to prove my masculinity is an exercise in futility, and that kind of pride turns people away from me. Humility allows me to rest knowing I am loved and accepted regardless of my physical or mental or musical or ministerial abilities. Humility draws people to me, not out of self-perceived pity (my prideful insistence that I don't need help) but invites them into a place of loving service to me that deeply blesses my soul.

Another perspective that brings humility in a most innocent and easy-to-accept way came by way of my 5-year-old grandson, Harry.

He was shown a picture of Melinda and me from our younger days and said, "Ga Ga and Grandma looked better then."

Reality is there are so many things I simply can no longer do... and I am good with that. I just need to remind myself that I have a young mind in an aging body and prioritize accordingly. It's ok for me to do nothing! Even though so many physical abilities have been taken from me, I would like to end this chapter and share this little-known humble brag about one still-intact ability (you'd think I had learned my lesson). Call it pride or call it a weird granddad trick, but despite Parkinson's, I can still wiggle my left ear. That's something...right?

SEVENTEEN
MORE WITH MELINDA

"Happy is the man who finds a true friend, and far happier is he who finds that true friend in his wife."

— FRANZ SCHUBERT

"A good marriage would be between a blind wife and a deaf husband."

— MICHEL DE MONTAIGNE

have the most incredible wife. She is truly my best friend and a constant source of encouragement to me. We are in this adventure called life together. We are a great team. I have shared this before, but it bears repeating. We are opposites in almost every possible way and that makes for a mystical, magical journey with very few dull moments.

The Michel de Montaigne quote above was one I saw lived out by my maternal great-grandparents, Joseph Willis Johnson and Celeste (Thorpe) Johnson. He was deaf and she was his ears. She was blind and he was her eyes. I recall many Christmas nights spent at their home in Sapulpa, Oklahoma. We would sing carols and listen to great-grandma Johnson tell the most vividly wild and funny stories of her childhood and beyond. We would sit in awe and wonder at the beautiful way in which our great grandparents so easily communicated and assisted one another with such grace, love, and dignity. It was as if their relationship was somehow facilitated by magic. She spoke for him when he could not understand/hear a question and he described to her what we each looked like so she could get a "glimpse" of how festive those Christmas nights were in a visual sense.

Melinda and I operate in much the same way. She is up when I am down and she helps me with encouragement. I am up when she is down and I try to do the same for her. I just like being with Melinda. She is both complete mystery to me and completely transparent with me. She is without guile and sees life very clearly as a blessing. She speaks whatever is on her mind, often leaving me in fits of laughter and leaving her bewildered at why I laughed at her statement. To be honest, she and I have been having Parkinson's moments for most of our 39 years of marriage!

Here is a prime example:

Sitting in our chairs one night, trying to decide what show to watch, Melinda suggested we watch Dirtiest Catch. I asked, "What is Dirtiest Catch? Some kind of new dating show?" She got tickled and began to giggle as she tried to explain herself. Her explanations made me laugh the most because she often has more than one explanation of what she is trying to convey. She meant to say, "Let's watch Deadliest Catch" but she got it mixed up with Dirty Jobs because Mike Rowe narrates both shows! We continued to giggle every few minutes as we watched Deadliest Catch, which we now refer to as Dirtiest Catch.

We have massive family instant message chats and hilarious video chats with our children and grandchildren. Melinda is one who always expresses her opinion. You always know where she stands on any issue or if she likes something. During one such conversation, we were discussing some of our favorite TV shows and movies and it became obvious to everyone that Melinda had a reason to dislike every single series and movie that had been mentioned.

One of the kids said with a laugh, "Mom, you don't like anything!" Melinda did not miss a beat, responding, "Sometimes I like things." That statement caused the children to laugh hysterically, and Melinda got tickled when she realized how that sounded. Melinda's innocent honesty makes me laugh so much and brings me endless moments of joy.

When we watch the news, which we honestly try to avoid, she voices her opinion with nothing but honesty. She could easily run the world. While watching crime dramas, she offers her opinion of what is going on, often, giving three or more outcomes. When we hear of someone's marriage breaking up — like a celebrity couple — she can give several reasons explaining why she thinks it fell apart, all while expecting me to listen to each explanation with my full attention. She is a natural-born teacher/lecturer of any subject!

One of my other favorite things about Melinda's way of thinking is her sleuthing skills. Moms just have a sixth sense and Melinda has whatever that is! I sometimes think she would make a great detective. Through the years, I have had my identity assumed, my images copied by others, and even had my name used in countless social media apps. Melinda hunts them down digitally and reports them. She has been highly successful in having them shut down. She is so proficient at it now that she can go on any given social media format and, within minutes, find several fake identities. She is single-handedly rescuing countless women who fall for these ruses. She is truly Sherlocka Holmes!

Here is another example of how she makes me laugh without trying. I recently left her a note that said, "I am so glad you are mine. I love you."

She emailed me, "Thanks for me note."

I wrote her back after I stopped laughing, "When did you start speaking pirate?"

EIGHTEEN
PARKINSON'S: NO JOKING MATTER...OR IS IT?

"It is requisite for the relaxation of the mind that we make use, from time to time, of playful deeds and jokes."

— THOMAS AQUINAS

I might as well get this out on the table. I LOVE jokes. Especially of the "dad" variety. One of my favorite things to do is tell jokes to my grandchildren and watch their response as it sinks in. I love their "I should have known that one" head slaps and their attempts to keep from cracking a smile and withhold their laughter. Hearing them moan and groan as they utter, "Grandpa…" gives me great pleasure.

Here's one I made up for my grandchildren. Even the older ones enjoy it even though they pretend not to!

"Knock Knock."
"Who's there?"
"Who."
"Who who?"
"Are you an owl?"

Melinda and I have a 20-acre wooded area we have built up with two miles of trails, each named for a grandchild and denoted by a real street sign, a campground, and a cedar tree we keep decorated throughout the year because in grandpa's and grandma's magical forest of Bren, it is Christmas all year 'round.

We have filled the forest with statues of real and mythical creatures and one of my favorite things is to occasionally switch the direction a certain statue is facing so the children will notice something different each time they visit the forest. My explanation is the longest-running prank ever. I simply tell them the creatures come alive at night and return to their statue form at dawn...and the grandchildren absolutely believe it!

They also know that on their birthday, they will be receiving a message from Ollie the Owl who resides in the forest we call Bren. With that message comes a note and clues, riddles and maps they must decode to find Ollie. They know that finding Ollie on their birthday means finding a five-dollar bill under Ollie's feet! These moments are some of my dearest treasures.

Also, in the forest of Bren, there is a white goose named Gilly. When one of the children finds Gilly, they are to take a picture with Gilly and send it to the other grandchildren. That grandchild then hides Gilly anywhere they choose in the vast forest as a challenge for the other grandchildren to try and find. Simple but effective incentive to go on wild excursions in search of a silly goose named Gilly.

In addition to jokes, I love a well-thought-out prank if it does not harm someone. Recently (I could not help myself) I came up with what I call one of my "evil grandpa" plans...meaning it is a bit scary, but wildly intriguing to my grandchildren. I bought a life-sized skeleton and devised a unique way of introducing said skeleton to the grandchildren, using their parents as part of the prank/joke. I first sent the following text to my entire family:

Me: "Hey everybody. Yesterday, for about two hours, the Gator was missing. Does anybody know what happened to it? I went to check last night and it was back in the barn. Just curious."

Daughter: "I noticed it was gone when letting June (the dog) out but thought you had it."

Me: "I never used it."

Another daughter: "Maybe we need to have [my husband] put one of his cameras pointing at the little barn."

Me: "I just got this private text message from an unknown number: 'It was me! Have fun trying to catch me, lol!'"

Daughter: "What?!"

Melinda: "What?!"

Me: "You might not want to share this next part with the kids. The culprit just sent me a picture." That picture was actually three pictures. Picture one shows the skeleton "driving" the Gator through the forest. Picture two shows the skeleton sitting on a bench in the campground with one hand petting the head of Ollie the Owl. Picture three? A distant shot of the skeleton hiding somewhere in the forest. My adult kids responded with shock, which made me laugh even more because I had not expected to "get" them. I was just setting up a prank for the grands!

Daughter: "I was really worried. I'm all texting [my husband] and like we need to figure this out."

Melinda: "I was stressed…" Of course, she had already sleuthed herself into thinking it was some random stranger or someone escaped from a local prison, a druggie, or someone we know who is trying to scare us for some reason!

Daughter: "Oh my gosh! I got really afraid. I thought some random stole it and brought it back. Like who would do that?"

Me: "This makes me laugh so much. I can neither confirm nor deny [my son-in-law] as a known accomplice…"

Daughter: "I can. Lol. He never responded and then when I asked him he just smiled."

It did not take long for the grandchildren to begin sending me voice messages via WhatsApp:

Grandson: "Nice try. You can't trick us, grandpa."

Granddaughter: "Hey, grandpa! You can't trick us! Did you make that skeleton or did you buy it or bring it or...you can't trick us!"

Me: "Hey, grandchildren. I think I tricked you very well. The problem is I don't know where that skeleton came from. All I know is he likes to drive the Gator. All I know is he likes to play pranks on children. I'm gonna try to figure out his name and where he came from. Just beware..."

Grandson: "I think maybe you should invite me over to help you find him. And I think, since I'm fast, if we see him once, I think I can catch him."

Granddaughter: "Grandpa, invite me over so I can catch the skeleton and I really want to figure out his name WITH you and, if I do, I want to throw that skeleton away! Bye!"

Grandson: "Grandpa, I don't like skeletons!"

Daughter of scared grandson: "He literally asks to drive by or walk by the 'big skeletons' (in our neighborhood during Halloween) every day, ha, ha! His mind changes each day."

I don't know why, but I love laughing. I never laugh at the misfortune of others or in such a way as to belittle another, but I find great healing comes to my soul via laughter and a healthy soul translates to a healthier physical body. It feels very cathartic to joke about my Parkinson's moments and it does not bother me when others tell me jokes specific to PD. Here is a brief smattering of jokes people have sent to me.

Joke: What do you call a cow with Parkinson's disease?
Punchline: Beef jerky.

Joke: What do you call a religious man with Parkinson's?

Punchline: A Quaker.

Joke: I saw people collecting for Parkinson's and they were shaking tins, which I thought was insensitive.

Joke: My friend told me this hilarious joke about Parkinson's last night, but I don't want to tell it because I'm a little shaky on the details.

Joke: My friend asked me the other day if I had any advice for dealing with Parkinson's. Apparently "just shake it off" wasn't the right answer.

For some reason, joking about something so serious helps take the dread and despair and sense of inevitability of my death out of the equation. It helps me live in the moment. Everyone dies. I just choose to die happy with a joyful attitude by living…and dying…well.

Just to bring you up to date on Ezra's plot to murder me…it thickens. For almost a year, we have worked together in my studio. He works a full-time job building guitar pedals and is simultaneously building his own company, having invented an amazing mic pre-amp. He works at a genius level, creating stunningly intricate circuit boards while I pitter away at my writing projects and music with a PD-clouded brain. After a couple of hours one recent morning, he got up, put on his jacket, and said to me, "I am stepping out for a few minutes. I hope you enjoy the next five minutes."

Concerned somewhat by the tone of his voice, I asked if he had planted a bomb somewhere in the studio.

He just smiled and waved goodbye as he walked out of the studio. It sounds kind of crazy, but I am quite intrigued at just how he might finally pull it off. His scare tactics are working. More on that later…

NINETEEN
MIGHT AS WELL BE HAPPY

"Most folks are as happy as they make up their minds to be."

— ABRAHAM LINCOLN

"I, not events, have the power to make me happy or unhappy today. I can choose which it shall be. Yesterday is dead, tomorrow hasn't arrived yet. I have just one day, today, and I'm going to be happy in it."

— GROUCHO MARX

Recently, I was sharing with a friend a joke my son had told me:

Dad: "Doctor! Doctor! You've gotta help me! All my sons want to be valets when they grow up!"
Doctor: "Looks like they've got Parking Sons Disease!"

I then shared with that friend how my son went on to ask me a very important question after sharing that joke. I realize I have already shared this story, but it helps make a point. He asked me if

I would mind if he went as me for Halloween. I told him that would be fine with me. He said he planned to wear his normal clothes and just walk around with a tremoring right hand! I loved the idea, but my son ultimately felt others may find his impersonation of me offensive, so he chose not to go as me.

My friend then said to me, "Ya'll have a great attitude!"

My response? "Any other attitude sucks." I always have a choice about what I think and my attitude. I can either be sad and depressed or I can be joyful and happy. I might as well be happy!

Several years ago, I wrote a song called, "Might As Well Be Happy." It seems as if it had been written all those years ago for this moment and these circumstances. You can listen to the song on YouTube later. Here's the story behind it:

This song came on June 30, 2011, as one of those spur-of-the-moment happenings. Feeling happy has not always come easily for me. Because of lies I had believed about my identity and about my worth and about my purpose in life, I have battled depression throughout my life. I am so glad to say that I am honestly happy even though I now have Parkinson's. Why? Because I have learned that life is not easy, but life can be enjoyed regardless of my pain, sorrow, suffering, circumstances, or what others think of me.

My point of view changed. I now live my life trying to see every aspect of my life from God's point of view. From my vantage point I often only see the bad, but God (being a very good God) only wants my best and can take even the harshest turns of life and make something beautiful of them.

My hope is not in what I can do or in what people think of me. My hope is not in money or in success or fame. My hope comes from knowing my Creator wastes nothing of my life if I simply turn to Him with whatever I am facing. His point of view is much more hopeful than mine.

This song came as I thought about how much joy I have in my life. When joy is the foundation, happiness is the result. My joy is in knowing God. Whether you believe like I do or not, allow the joyful attitude of this song to brighten your day.

The ukulele seemed the most obvious and happy instrument for the song. The whistle is all me. I purposely wanted to sound like a little boy whistling in response to the joy set before him as he explores his way to his favorite fishing hole.

The pictures used to create the video were drawn by me. My vision was to draw the scenes with crayons from the viewpoint of a young child. We adults tend to make life much too complicated. I am a man...but somewhere deep inside is a small boy with big happy dreams. Life is simple for me now. I love God. He loves me. I love others. Others love me. Happiness is a choice.

Life is a journey we are meant to enjoy regardless of our circumstances. The words of this song have taken on a whole new meaning for me since I first received it. In January of 2019, I was diagnosed with Parkinson's disease. It rocked my world and caused me to question so much of what I believe about God and His love for me. My conclusion? He is so good and so loving that He can use even Parkinson's for my good and for His glory. I can honestly say having Parkinson's has revealed a whole new level of joy to my life. My greatest joy of all? I am never alone. He is with me!

Though the fig tree should not blossom
   And there be no fruit on the vines,
   Though the yield of the olive should fail
   And the fields produce no food,
   Though the flock should be cut off from the fold
   And there be no cattle in the stalls,
   Yet I will exult in the LORD,
   I will rejoice in the God of my salvation.
   The Lord GOD is my strength,
   And He has made my feet like hinds' feet,
   And makes me walk on my high places.

— HABAKKUK 3:17-19 NASB

Hear and watch the song at https://youtu.be/ZTOInRI4KH8 or search for "Might As Well Be Happy" by Dennis Jernigan on YouTube.

Might As Well Be Happy
June 30, 2011

Verse
It's a big, big world
Full of big, big trials
Full of big, big hurts
Full of weary miles
I heard a wise man say
To every girl and boy,
"To live a big, big life
You have a big, big choice!"

Pre-Chorus
You might as well be happy!
You might as well rejoice!
You might as well be happy
If you're given a choice!
You might as well be happy!
Might as well rejoice!
You might as well be happy
If you're given a choice!

Chorus
You might as well be happy!
The sun is still here shining,
Though the rain be blinding,
Though the wind blow strong!
You can focus on the darkness!
And you can focus on the pain and loss

Or you can see beyond!

Verse
Here's a little truth:
There's a big, big God
With a big, big love
Enough for one and all
He can take a mountain
In your way so tall
Show you how He sees it
Make it very small!

Pre-Chorus
I might as well be happy!
I might as well rejoice!
I might as well be happy
If I'm given the choice!
I might as well be happy!
Might as well rejoice!
I might as well be happy
If I'm given a choice!

Chorus
I might as well be happy!
The sun is still here shining
Though the rain be blinding
Though the wind blow strong!
I can focus on the darkness!
And I can focus on the pain and loss
Or I can see beyond

Verse
There's a big, big world
With a big, big sky
With a big adventure

Where you learn to fly!
Whether good or bad times
You can spread your wings
Rise above the darkness
To what the sunlight brings!

I might as well be happy!
I might as well be happy!
I might as well be happy!
I might as well be happy!

I might as well be
I might as well be

TWENTY
A CAREGIVER'S POINT OF VIEW

"I would go to the deeps a hundred times to cheer a downcast spirit. It is good for me to have been afflicted, that I might know how to speak a word in season to one that is weary."

— CHARLES SPURGEON

"Nobody cares how much you know, until they know how much you care."

— THEODORE ROOSEVELT

asked my wife to write a chapter for this book from her perspective as caregiver and wife of a husband with Parkinson's (HWP). Her response was perfect for the nature of this book. "I am not a writer. I will send you the bullet points and you write the chapter for me." So, as Melinda's ghostwriter, following is Melinda's suggestions for those who serve as caregivers for GWWP (Ghost Writers With Parkinson's). Did I mention I have PD? Is it lost on anyone to think about the trust Melinda places in me, one who experiences occasional brain fog and the occasional "Why did I come into this room?" moments, to write her chapter for her? She really does make me believe I can do anything...mostly...

From Melinda:

I see myself as Dennis' most vocal cheerleader. It is my place to remind him what he has and not what he has lost. In our home we do not allow circumstances — even PD — to define us. We both take great care in speaking words of blessing over one another, and we choose to believe that God wastes nothing and that He will use even PD for our good. Just as God is FOR us, we are FOR one another. I am his advocate and Dennis is mine.

We hear the old adage, "Sticks and stones may break my bones, but words will never hurt me," without realizing just how wrong that so-called wisdom really is. As believers in and followers of Jesus Christ, we have replaced that way of thinking with the following wisdom from God's Word:

"Death and life are in the power of the tongue..."

— PROVERBS 18:21 NASB

The words we speak can bring death to a vision or they can bring life to a vision. They can bring discouragement or encouragement. When someone suffers from Parkinson's, their cognitive abilities are often affected. Dennis calls moments of mental fogginess "Parkinson's moments." The last thing he needs is for me to speak words that come across as impatient or words that negatively affect his attempt at expressing his thoughts verbally. To do so is the equivalent of telling him what he is trying to express to me is of no value, and this kills a little part of his soul, often causing him to withdraw from situations and people that he needs in his life. The words we speak to one another really do have the power of life and death.

On that note: PD is NOT a death sentence! It is simply a part of life that God is allowing us to go through. We can either choose to face it with joy and grace or we can choose to face it with despair and depression. It is imperative that we caregivers recognize that we have a choice as to what we think and that every feeling we have is produced by a thought we have had. It is imperative that Dennis and I see ourselves as a team. As team members we try to applaud one another with words of positive affirmation. When Dennis does something that blesses me in some way, like loading the dishwasher or taking the trash out or getting a Jeopardy question right (I still do not understand how he knows so much and is able to recall so much minutiae while forgetting why I sent him to the store (for AAA batteries), I verbally encourage him with, "Way to go, babe!" or "How in the world can you KNOW that answer?!" Always err on the side of positive.

One of the most wearying tasks as a caregiver is to go for several days of remaining positive whenever Dennis goes through occasional seasons of being overwhelmed or swamped in negative thinking. If I am not careful, I can get dragged down those rabbit holes of negative thoughts and fear about the future with him. Again, the best thing I can do for both of us is to speak truths, reaffirm the reality, and kick the negative unrealistic thinking to the curb.

I am naturally a positive thinker, but I occasionally grow weary in trying to keep Dennis buoyed up in the Parkinson's moments. What is so annoying, but funny, are the times when I get down in some way and Dennis simply asks me, "What would you tell me to do? What would you tell me to think on?" Around our house we call negative thoughts stinkin' thinkin'! Ain't nobody got time for that!

As a mom of nine and a grandmother of 13, I am a natural born nurturer. I have an Alpha Female personality. Dennis is still overly — I mean that in a positive way — creative, finding great joy and something to look forward to as he continues to write music and books and encourage others via social media. Yet, he has moments of mental fogginess and loss of physical stamina. It is during such moments that I tend to want to mother and nurture him rather than be his wife...and I am NOT his mother!

It is imperative that I remind myself he is a grown-ass man who is still capable of much. He does not need me hovering over him worrying about his every movement or activity. I also remind myself to give him a bit of extra time to complete tasks and to give him time to finish sentences without jumping in and speaking for him. I am learning to be a better listener rather than a smothering mother who comes across as impatient and insensitive to what he is trying to communicate. Sometimes, it is in the patience I extend to him as a listener — making him feel his words are worth my time — that best communicates my love and care for him.

When I was growing up, teasing and joking were often used as forms of manipulation and abuse. Being married to a now 64-year-old man who still loves to tease and prank and scare his children and grandchildren...a man who seems to thrive on his children and grandchildren teasing, joking, and pranking him...has brought much healing to my life.

He gives himself permission to play and have fun. He is a master of and loves good puns. Caregivers need to do the same! I say laugh, have fun, and laugh some more! It is permissible to have a sense of humor about Dennis' journey through Parkinson's...OUR journey! Having a positive attitude and a good laugh when grandpa prays for dinner with the grandkids fighting to hold his "party hand" makes our lives joyful. I tend to be a glass half full kind of girl anyway, so this works for me. As a way to minister to me, Dennis and the family know when they have crossed the line with me when it comes to teasing. All I have to do is say, "I'm about to cry," and they know to stop.

One can never go wrong with finding something positive to say. I firmly believe we can find something positive in almost any everyday situation. This is one of those "ALL things" the Lord talks about in His Word in Romans 8:28. It will work for our good. God truly wastes nothing. I believe that!

One way we are practicing what we preach is to prepare for

end-of-life things. Dennis loves the movie Black Panther and the quote by T'Chaka, King of Wakanda, to his son and eventual heir to the throne, T'Challa: "A man who has not prepared his children for his own death has failed as a father."

We keep our children apprised of their dad's health and this helps lighten the load for me and for Dennis. Getting our affairs in order, updating our living trust and our wills, along with fine-tuning our DNR (Do Not Resuscitate) directives, are vital and we just brought ours up to date. By the time you read this, we will have selected and purchased burial plots. Dennis has even prepared a list of items he wants to leave certain children and grandchildren as well as preparing a list of songs for his eventual memorial service.

This is not morbid. It is actually freeing. Peace of mind is worth the momentary pain of making such plans. The children know exactly what to do if we require hospice or end-of-life treatment. They know exactly who gets what and where to dump our bodies (Ezra is the expert in this area due to his current plans to bring about his father's demise…just joking). I urge caregivers to not procrastinate. Be proactive in getting the big things prepared now so you can both enjoy your lives and your children and all the precious little things by living life in the present. So, you CAN be present in the here and now. Our children know our plans and are grateful for taking the burden off their shoulders.

One of the most vital things to me, as wife and caregiver to a HWP, is to share intimate moments…holding hands…a slow dance in the kitchen…singing our favorite songs together in the car… going to the occasional movie in a real theater and treating the popcorn and candy as our evening meal…a night on the town or dinner with close friends. Dennis and I keep doing the little things that keep the spark of intimacy burning brightly.

I saved this piece of advice for last. It should go without saying, but caregivers must be intentional about taking care of themselves. You can't adequately take care of meeting the needs of the one you care for if you do not take care of your own needs. It can be as simple as getting out of bed...getting dressed...brushing your teeth and hair...reading your Bible...journaling your thoughts... meditating on good things.

One of my favorite taking-care-of-myself activities is simply worshiping God. I take what I call "praise breaks" as often as needed. When having a hard day with the needs of my husband, I can step away for a few moments and praise God. Intimacy with God — exchanging life with Him — can be done anywhere, anytime, under any circumstance and can change the atmosphere from heavy and dark to joy and light. When raising our nine children, I took advantage of this practice every day! And I now have the privilege of teaching this same principle to our grandchildren. We include them in and encourage them to participate in caring for their grandfather. We sing with them and dance with them and teach them the songs we sang with their parents when they were children. And the grandchildren ask to sing these songs over and over, again and again! The best self-care ever...

I will close my portion of the book with these suggestions. Join a support group for caregivers of those with PD. If there is not one available near you, find an online group. That is what I do...and it helps me fight feelings of being alone in the battle with PD.

Practice creativity. Write that book you have always dreamed of writing. Paint that landscape of your dreams. Write an encouraging poem to that friend who is shut in. I make jewelry and unique gifts. A good portion of each day finds me creating earrings, bracelets, bookmarks, or necklaces using the most beautiful gold, silver, and bronze wires, adorning each piece with precious and semi-precious stones. I find great fulfillment in creating custom pieces for individuals as well as entire sets of matching pieces for bridal parties. Being creative fills my heart with great joy and I pray over each piece I create as a means of blessing those who will one day wear them. We are all created in God's image...and isn't He THE Creator? Just a thought...

Fellowship with those you are close to...book club...fitness group...tea party...church. Practice hospitality and see it as killing two birds with one stone. Church gatherings accomplish this for us. Dennis and I see our home as a hospital for hurting people, which is headed by the Great Physician, Jesus. We are even incorporated as a legal church, and we meet once a week in our home since Dennis can no longer tolerate large crowds for long periods of time. We not only provide a safe place for people to unburden their own souls but find a safe place to unburden our own.

TWENTY-ONE
NO WALK IN THE PARKINSON'S

To my editor: "Good luck, you've got your work cut out for you;
you haven't lived until you've edited a fantasy novel written by
someone with Parkinson's!"

— DENNIS JERNIGAN

People who know I have PD will often ask me how I am
doing. Occasionally I respond, "I am doing fine, but it's
no walk in the 'Park'inson's." Parkinson's is not is not an
easy thing to experience and is not pleasant. It is NOT a walk in
the park, but that doesn't mean my life has to be lived devoid of
joy, peace, or laughter! I have just chosen to see my life from a
different point of view since my life has become a walk in the
Parkinson's!

To say I do not experience moments of physical, mental, and
emotional suffering would be a lie. But I refuse to become so self-
focused on my unpleasant feelings that I bring harm to those I love
and I refuse to wallow in self-pity. Just as I say I plan to live well
and die well despite PD, I plan to enjoy my life and bring joy and
comfort to as many as possible along the way.

This book has not been a scientific treatise on Parkinson's and what causes it or an exhaustive explanation of PD. I am actually a bit shaky (pun intended) on the cause of and treatments for the illness. I know as much as my neurologist and various Parkinson's-related websites can tell me. What I am trying to say is this: I am no scientist, not a neurologist, and Parkinson's affects people differently. This is simply my journey through PD to this point in my life. Did I say that already? I believe I used almost those exact words near the beginning of this book. In fact, I am certain I have repeated myself occasionally throughout the book. Get over it. I have Parkinson's. Blame any blatant repetitions on my editor. God bless his ever-loving, patient heart!

And speaking of editors, even though I struggle with frequent brain fog, I still feel compelled to continue writing both books and music. This is the third book I have completed since my original diagnosis. With each submission of my final manuscript to my editor, I have felt the need to warn them and to ask for their patience due to my walk in the Parkinson's!

One of those books was a fantasy novel for young readers. You may be thinking to yourself, "That sounds like the perfect genre and target audience for someone with PD." Now that I think about it, you may be right to have such thoughts! That book, "The Puzzle," I have already mentioned but the email exchange between me and my editor might be of interest to you. At any rate, here is his response when I asked him if he would be willing to edit my book. I'll call him "Darren"...since that's his name:

Dennis,

It's so great to have this update from you. I am humbled by your humor and grace and it's an honor to work with you again. I'll shoot you a ballpark quote per usual in the next couple of weeks. Count me in and thank you for your continued kindness.

Darren

My Response:

Darren,

Good luck! You've got your work cut out for you! You haven't lived until you've edited a fantasy novel written by someone with Parkinson's!

I am so glad to know you can help me out once again! Writing this book has been a major challenge in that I have made the antagonist of the story a sorcerer named Sepeleo Parkinson. My goal is to teach my grandchildren what Parkinson's is and how they can help me battle the disease. While allegorical in nature, the spell he casts upon my character will be very clear to the reader what the effects of the disease are but in a very intriguing way...at least that's what I think, lol!

Your challenge is to edit a book written by someone with Parkinson's, lol! I may have written 90K words that are mush...or may prove to be best read when smoking weed!

I am also going to write a book describing my slog through Parkinson's and plan on calling the book Parkinson's and Recreation...because there are too many funny moments that have transpired since my diagnosis that I can't not share them.

In a following email, I wrote:

Darren,

I finished the book and it comes in at 105,055 words. I basically wrote the book for my grandchildren with the attitude of 'what would I want to say to my grandchildren about faith in an allegorical manner if this was the last book I ever wrote?' It is what it is, lol! I am waiting for my wife to read through the complete book before I send the manuscript your way.

It was quite a task to include all 12 of my grandchildren in the story and keep the story interesting and focused. It is a legacy book and a love letter to my grandchildren that I hope will challenge them as they grow into adults and my hope is that it would provide at least some financial blessing throughout their lives for generations to come. What I am trying to say is 'good luck' at trying to edit this thing, lol!

Blessings,

DJ

Before "The Puzzle," I wrote a book called "The Middle of Nowhere." This book recounts the many moments in my life when I felt abandoned in the middle of nowhere and PD was the catalyst. Here is what I wrote to Darren concerning the editing of that book:

Darren,

One of my main concerns with the book is that I not come off sounding like a victim...of persecution or of Parkinson's or of anything. My goal is to lead people to see that God is with them in the middle of nowhere. I share many instances in my life I have never shared publicly. I don't know if all those instances are necessary to the book. I don't want to over-share. Help me by letting me know if there are any segments that you think I should consider cutting from the book. I have attached the title song from the book's companion recording. It expresses my heart as it relates to all I have experienced in my life. I thought it might inspire you a bit...

Darren's response:

Dennis,

Thanks for this extra context and for the song. Will listen tonight. And I will definitely keep an eye out for potential over-sharing. Glad to know your heart on that - very helpful!

Darren

Something very interesting happened when "The Middle of Nowhere" came out. Soon after the book was released, Melinda and I went for my yearly checkup with my neurologist. He asked me how I was doing and what limitations I was experiencing. We talked of tremors and brain fog and constipation. You know. Normal stuff. Both Melinda and I shared how we are choosing to see PD from the Lord's point of view and how we are choosing to be happy and walk in joy despite PD…of how we had chosen to not allow PD to define or limit our lives…of how we are choosing to use it for good. He replied, "I wish all my patients had the attitude you and your wife exude! Attitude is everything!" Feeling very affirmed, I went on to tell him of the book I had written since my last checkup.

No sooner had I uttered these words than he said, "You wrote a book?! You're kidding me! What's the title?!" My neurologist seemed shocked that I could have written a book while suffering with PD! He was so taken aback that he looked it up on Amazon DURING my exam and ordered the book for himself! This, of course, is all part of my master plan — a new method of marketing involving one medical specialist at a time.

As of this writing, my son Ezra's plans for my murder have not yet been realized. And I have to admit, I am kind of curious just what he has finally come up with. Poison? Crossbow accident? Scooter accident during a local patriotic parade? Jousting mishap or swordsman's unfortunate accidental slaying of spectator or falconry demonstration gone terribly awry at the Renaissance Faire? Who knows?! The joy is in not knowing!

Meanwhile, Ezra and I continue to have fun with wordplay, as I do with all my children. He bowls each Sunday. Recently, his mom and I wanted to watch him bowl, so I asked him to let us know his next game time. What follows is our text exchange. It brings me a lot of joy:

Ezra: I'll be bowling today! I'll be there 11-1, y'all can come for all of it or just what you want to :)
Melinda: We plan on being there!
Me: We'll bowl you over with our presence.
Ezra: I can't wait haha

Me: I just don't want to get pin-ned into the parking lot by the crowds of bowling fans.

Ezra: I'll spare you the trouble and save you a spot

Me: I know you're thinking to yourself, "Spare me!" Great minds...

I'll just stay in my lane.

Ezra: Get your mind out of the gutter

Me: I think I may have gone over the line with that last one. It takes balls to be a good bowler...

Ezra: That's a strike if I've ever seen one haha

Me: It was a bit of a turkey...which I hope you get many of today, lol! I bet your favorite Gerard Butler movie is 300...

Ezra: I'm on lane 8! Turning my phone to airplane mode!

He knows how to bring a pun-fest to a much-needed conclusion. I will try to do the same for you. I would like to bring this chapter to a conclusion by sharing some of the personal thoughts of some of my adult children regarding how PD has affected them. It has been, by no means, a walk in the park for them either.

"Live so that when your children think of fairness, caring, and integrity, they think of you."

— H. JACKSON BROWN, JR.

Dad,

My main thoughts about you and Parkinson's: I feel helpless and distant from it. I really wish I could help in some way, and it's hard not knowing what to do besides showing you I care and love you whenever we speak.

The way you've handled everything regarding Parkinson's is truly inspiring to me. You have been open and honest about the struggles and at the same time shown an amazing amount of strength and resilience. I look up to you so much. The way you carry yourself and show so much love is how I want to be. I love you, dad.

J

Hey Dad,

For me, I didn't really understand what it would mean when I first heard you had it. It made me sad at first - but being able to watch you go through this journey and the way that you have handled it has given me a new perspective. I am not sad. I am grateful for the time I get to spend with you, regardless of what health issues you have to deal with...you are still my dad. I don't see you as anything other than that - I don't see PD as who you are or even one of the major defining factors of who you are.

I have learned so much wisdom from you and I feel able to navigate life's challenges in a healthier way because of you and how you live your life. That is how you having PD has affected me.

Thanks,
Ezra

Dad,

It had been 4.5 years since I last saw you, and 3 years since your PD diagnosis. Our last trip home this year was a lot for me.

To be honest, I was really scared. I didn't know how much it had changed you. I hadn't even seen you tremor. I didn't know what you weren't/were capable of. I had no idea...It was terrifying for me.

When I saw you, as I walked through those airport security gates, all I saw was my dad. But, the days and weeks that followed have still left me trying to come to terms with how you have changed, how we as a family have changed. Change isn't a negative word, and I don't want you to feel that I see that change negatively. It was just a lot (and still is!) to process.

The last time I saw you, when I left (in 2017) you had zero tremors, you had a voice, you were present at game nights, and so involved in every single thing. That's how I expected you to be. Even when we FaceTimed over these last several years since your diagnosis, it was always when you were "good". It was hard for me to realize what the rest of my siblings have already come to know - the progression of the illness. I walked smack dab into the reality of it.

I think my first fight (there was only 1 after that, so I think we did ok!) with mom after seeing you the first time, was on day 2 of us being back in the states and she mentioned you may never come to Australia again. I broke down, shut down, and she said I was dismissing her when she was trying to be honest with me. I told her if I was being dismissive, it was more me just having travelled to a different hemisphere and seeing PD in the face for the first time, and her laying that on me isn't just an easy thing to process at 7 in the morning, after 30 hours of travel with two children.

I actually hate that I had that interaction with mom, and wish I could do it over again, and be kinder...but it was a smack in the face for me for what my future was and what reality is. I already feel so far away, so removed from the daily life everyone lives (and PD is just a daily part of that for everyone), and seeing what PD is in person was incredibly confronting for me. The rest of the family has seen it for YEARS. I had two days. BUT - What followed those two days was magic.

I saw a man who reserved every ounce of energy for his grandchildren. A man who did everything in his power to make our trip full of memories, to pack in year's worth of lost time and jam it into a few weeks. I won't forget (and neither will my girls) what those weeks meant.

I may have missed you at game nights, but my kids got to experience you at your fullest...the man I know and adore...who makes every single thing fun and adventurous. A man who had a knighting ceremony [for his grandchildren], two crazy-ass bon fires (I'm glad the parents were there to supervise because you just chased and played with the grandkids the whole time. Haha!), let us face paint him for our firework shopping event, who swam, played, watched movies, dried tears, mediated family drama, drove thousands of kilometers (I'm sure) on the Gator, went bowling, sang The Greatest Showman…all of that just to bring his grandchildren joy.

My girls didn't hesitate or balk at your tremor, they most likely fought over who got to hold your "party hand". They saw it as a superpower. They saw you as a king, the leader of Bren, the champion, the dreamer, the fun master…exactly how I always saw you. How I see you.

Thank you for the energy you saved for my kids. You don't know what that means to me. I get to lay down my own desire to have you stay up until 1 am, and give way to my girls getting to experience the magic and wonder of having you in their lives.

There's so many more words I could say, I could probably write an entire book. But, I feel it's important for you to know how much I treasured those weeks. Those days where you had to give up time with me so you could give your time to my children. Thank you. Honestly, from the bottom of my heart, I am so grateful. Thank you.

Hannah

TWENTY-TWO
IN CLOSING

"Some people walk in the rain, others just get wet."

— ROGER MILLER

"The tragedy of life is not death but what we let die inside of us while we live."

— NORMAN COUSINS

L ife has moments of despair, hardship, pain, and suffering. I know those feelings all too well, but I refuse to allow them to define me or stop living my life to the fullest. I plan on going down in grand fashion. I will play Nerts with my grandchildren until my brain hurts. I will take them fishing even if all I do is untangle their tangled fishing lines. I will welcome the faux murder plots and enjoy the pun-ishment my children put me through as a result of PD. I will shower love upon their mother/grandmother with random moments of PDA, as an example of how love lays down its life for the one it loves, even if tremors aren't of the romantic nature!

I will always kiss my wife goodnight. I will always slow dance with her. I will always make my grandchildren feel like the only people in the room. I will always be available to my children. I will always sing, even if raspy whispers of joy are all I am able to manage. I will always put Christ first in my life and will always choose to see my life and PD from His point of view.

I will play in the rain. I will view the vast flatness of the prairie with the same awe and wonder I view the majestic rise of a lofty mountain peak. I will live my life with childlike wonder. I will always laugh at the jokes my children and grandchildren make up.

"Where do girls go for vacation?" Answer: "To Girl Land!"

I will always choose hope. Always choose joy. Always choose good thoughts to permeate my mind, whether I eventually experience dementia or not. I may one day lose my marbles, but what fun it will be in trying to find them!

Life is best lived from the vantage point of the One Who made us. From His lofty perspective, my foggy brain sees life more clearly. Feels love more deeply. Finds gratitude in the most mundane and ridiculous ways and places. Who would have known trying to solve my own fake murder at the hands of one of my own children could be so invigorating or that looking around every corner for who might jump out to frighten me could bring such life-filling joy?!

Life is a grand adventure and PD is but one blip on the screen of the grand scheme of that mysterious, magical, imagination-fueling, thrill-inducing, wonderful journey! And best of all? I get to share it with those who matter most to me. My wife. My children. My grandchildren. My extended family. My friends. And most of all, with my God Who loves me massively and Who never once leaves me to walk this journey apart from Him.

PD is, at worst, an inconvenience and an annoyance. At its best, it is a catalyst to unexpected joy and peace and freedom and love I never anticipated. Parkinson's has brought a deeper awareness of what is most important to me and in a very real sense, brought my soul a refreshing re-creation along the grand adventure of life.

A bonus? Believe it or not, Oklahoma has more than its fair share of earthquakes (and you thought tornados were our biggest threat), but I rarely feel them because I find it difficult to determine the difference between the earth's tremors and my PD-induced tremors! This takes fear off the table for me as far as earthquakes are concerned! See what I did there?

By now, you see where I'm going with this. I hope I haven't shaken you up too much...or maybe I hope I have! At any rate, I hope you feel refreshed, reinvigorated, and your soul bathed in re-creation of the vantage point of another man's perspective. If given the choice of despair or happiness...might as well be happy!

I have to tell you about one last Parkinson's moment that happened just this morning. I feel my mind is truly re-created each time I experience one of these moments because I love to laugh... and God knows that...and He uses it for healing to my soul.

After my morning workout, I stripped, took off my glasses, grabbed my toothbrush and put a dab of toothpaste on it from a new tube I had just opened yesterday and jumped in the shower (I find jumping in the shower much more fun than just standing there...). While brushing my teeth in the shower, the toothpaste tasted a bit off and felt a bit like lotion, leaving the feeling of a slight film on my teeth. I chalked it up to the way Parkinson's can sometimes cloud my senses.

Once I had dried off and put my glasses back on, the toothpaste filmy feeling continued to bug me. I opened the drawer where I keep my toothpaste and other toiletries and quickly found the problem. The "toothpaste" was actually a tube of anti-itch creme for poison ivy! Both tubes were of similar size and color. I had just picked up the wrong one. But my teeth have not itched at all today...and so it continues...

About Parkinson's and Recreation: It is what it is. Even as I write those words, I ask myself the question, "If it is what it is, what the heck is it?" Maybe this will help clear things up for you:

"How do you greet someone with Parkinson's?"

"What's shakin'?"

Sorry. Couldn't shake that one last urge to leave you with a joke...

The End...for now...

DID YOU ENJOY THIS BOOK?

Did you enjoy this book? You can make a big difference by leaving a review.

Reviews are one of the most important ways authors reach new readers. I don't have the funds to reach new people through advertising, but I have something more valuable: a group of individuals who support and believe in my ministry.

If you enjoyed this book, would you consider leaving an honest review? It doesn't need to be long. Your review will help other readers find this book.

To leave a review, simply visit your preferred book vendor where you purchased your copy of this book and leave your review.

BECOME A DJ INSIDER

Would you like to receive email newsletters from me? You'll receive periodic news, updates, offers, and prayer requests. There's no obligation and I'll never spam you. Don't miss out on another update! Visit www.dennisernigan.com/newsletter to sign up.

You can also find me on Patreon to get daily devotions, music, new releases, and exclusive updates. Check out all the benefits at www.patreon.com/dennisjernigan

ALSO BY DENNIS JERNIGAN

FANTASY BOOKS BY BY DENNIS JERNIGAN

The Chronicles of Bren

A fantasy adventure series for young adults

Captured: The Chronicles of Bren: Book One

Sacrifice: The Chronicles of Bren: Book Two

Generations: The Chronicles of Bren: Book Three

The Bairns of Bren

A fantasy adventure series for young readers; for the young at heart!

Hide and Seek: The Bairns of Bren: Book One

The Light Eater: The Bairns of Bren: Book Two

The Puzzle: The Bairns of Bren: Book Three

SHORT STORIES FOR CHILDREN

The Incredible Growing Basketball Goal

Daddy's Song

The Christmas Dream

OTHER BOOKS BY DENNIS JERNIGAN

Sing Over Me (autobiography)

Renewing Your Mind: Identity and the Matter of Choice

The Middle of Nowhere

Daily Devotions For Kingdom Seekers, Vol I, II, and III

This Is My Destiny

Giant Killers: Crushing Strongholds, Securing Freedom in Your Life

The Short Life

MUSIC

Fun Songs & Lullabies

Find all of Dennis Jernigan's 25+ music recordings at www.dennisjernigan.com

Listen to The Dennis Jernigan Podcast to hear the stories behind his songs.

WHO IS DENNIS JERNIGAN?

Dennis Jernigan is a song writer and author who, with his wife Melinda, makes his home in northeastern Oklahoma very near where these stories were first inspired. They have raised nine children together and now enjoy many grandchildren..

Foremost known for his Christian praise music, Jernigan has extended his creativity to the realm of authoring books.

Fantasy reached him with hope during a very rough period in his life, and he feels a sense of urgency to write stories that will inspire others. The stories found within the pages of these books are a legacy to the generations to come.

For more information:
www.dennisjernigan.com
mail@dennisernigan.com
(918)781-1200

facebook.com/therealdennisjernigan
twitter.com/dennisjernigan
instagram.com/dennisjernigan
youtube.com/dennisjernigan

Printed in the USA
CPSIA information can be obtained
at www.ICGtesting.com
LVHW012253100224
771523LV00003B/562

9 781948 772211